I Must Tell You Something

Arno Bo

Bloomsbury

Edited by Susan Dickinson

First published in Great Britain in 1996
Bloomsbury Publishing PLC, 2 Soho Square, London W1V 6HB

A CIP catalogue record for this book is available from The British Library

Pb ISBN O 7475 2514 5

Text design by AB3
Printed in Great Britain by Cox and Wyman, Reading, Berkshire

10 9 8 7 6 5 4 3 2 1

For Rosemyn

The love you met
gave you courage
to look at death –
courage of that love,
in which you will ever
and ever see Mum herself.

Sunday, December 13th

WE'VE PLAYED with the kittens for an hour. Phoebe is crazy about them. She wants to hug them all the time and have them on her lap.

Leon won't play with us. He's seventeen today and too grown up, of course. He's our cousin, but I wish he were my brother. The kittens belong to my other cousins: Elise and Rachel.

We've had Coke and crisps, and I think I can smell sausage rolls in the oven, but no, we are going home because Dad has had the flu and he doesn't feel too well.

Anyway, the kittens have just jumped through their catdoor into the garage, and Mum is coming out. My mother is the dearest and most beautiful Mum in the world: she has goldish hair and big, honest eyes that always know everything. She talks to Aunt Laura while Dad waits impatiently in the car. Then we drive away.

It's pitch dark tonight. Next week will be the shortest day of the year – all cosy and snug. I always turn on the lights early and draw the curtains. Then we have hot chocolate. And a hot-water bottle in bed.

The road is very quiet and it's also quiet in the car; we are all tired – just staring into the blackness. It's drizzling.

Monday tomorrow. I hate school. But it's Christmas next week. I'm going to sing in the choir, on stage! And Phoebe is going to be an angel.

I'm sitting behind Mum, leaning on the front seat – a good place to suck my thumb and watch the road, to see everything.

Sometimes I see more than Dad, because I don't have to steer. Now and then he looks at me in the mirror and we wink at each other.

It's pretty boring outside because…

'Hey, watch out, Dad!'

What is he doing? Look in front of you, Dad!

There is a bend in the road but he doesn't steer round it, he keeps on going straight…

We hit something and are all thrown about. It hurts and I feel sick.

Dad turns the wheel wildly now. What's he doing? I want to help, to scream, to crawl away, but I feel like lead. I can't do anything.

The world is falling over me. I'm lost.

Silence. Darkness.

There was a bang. Right through me. I still feel it. Where am I?

It's so dark and silent.

Pain.

Inside me the banging goes on. Where are we?

Still in the car.

I want to get out but I can't move. I'm stuck. Nobody

moves. If only this pain would go away.

How long have we been there?

Somebody is coming. She looks into the car.

'What's your name?' she asks.

'Rosemyn.'

'And your sister?'

'Phoebe.'

'We've called for help. They'll be here very soon.'

She is holding my hand.

'My arm hurts,' I say. 'Has this really happened?'

Something bad must have happened.

Phoebe has fallen forward and her head is funny. She isn't moving. Where are Mum and Dad? It's so dark. The woman puts Phoebe's head straight. Then Phe throws up. But she doesn't say anything and her eyes are closed.

I hear sirens. There are people everywhere. They are all talking at once and running up and down.

A window is taken out of the car. Cold. Slowly they move something and I am lifted out. My arm still hurts.

Now a man is holding me.

'How old are you?' he asks.

'Nine.'

'When are you going to be ten?'

'In August.'

'And how old is your sister?'

'Six.'

He says: 'I have two daughters myself.'

'Not to the hospital, not to the hospital,' I say.

The sirens and lights are everywhere.

'I don't want an injection.'

Who are they? What are they doing? All these people – there must be a hundred, running and talking anxiously…

A huge lamp is turned on. I shut my eyes.

Has this really happened?

Someone puts me down. Then I am lifted into a big car.

'Don't take me to the hospital. No!'

'What's your name?' asks another man.

'Where do you live?'

'Which school do you go to?'

But I can see blood.

'Please don't talk about it,' I say. 'It's horrible…'

'I'm going to give you an injection,' says the man. 'Everything will be all right. We'll take good care of you.'

He stays beside me all the time. I'm so tired. It's an ambulance and I've never been so tired.

'Blood on the floor… Don't talk about it.'

Why is it taking so long? Where are Mum and Dad, and Phoebe?

Drive slowly, I want to say, we've just had an accident.

He seems to be driving very fast.

I'd like to sleep, but that is frightening too.

I'm in the hospital.

The others are injured too. That's why nobody's come to take me home.

Doctors and nurses keep coming in to examine me.

They tell me what happened: we crashed into a tree. It was a serious accident. These words stick in my head.

There are pieces of glass in my face; they are taken out. I don't really notice how much it hurts.

Photos are taken that show everywhere in my body: x-rays. My arm is broken in a difficult spot, near my shoulder. A nurse stays with me and she gives me a little white felt dog.

Luckily I can still suck my thumb. It's my other arm they put in a sling.

What are we waiting for now?

The door opens and Gran and Grandad come in. Why are they here?

'We crashed! I *told* Dad: "Watch out!"'

They know. That's why they are here, because Mum and Dad are injured.

Mum is in a different hospital, in Denton.

'Why isn't she here?' I ask.

'It's difficult for a hospital to handle four casualties at the same time, especially on a Sunday.'

She'll be all right, of course. That's what hospitals are for. The man said so. But when are we going to see Mum? And when are we going home?

Gran and Grandad are talking with the doctors. Uncle John and Aunt Laura have come now.

I watch their faces and then I'm not so sure... Will it really be all right?

'What has happened to Mum?'

'She's quite badly hurt, mostly to her head and

stomach. It's rather serious, I'm afraid.'

'How?'

'She is too ill to be moved.'

I want to ask more but I don't dare.

'And Phoebe?'

'She has a kind of concussion.'

'And Dad?'

'A broken leg and something wrong with his chest.'

They are careful, trying not to talk, not to be sad.

'What *I've* got is worst, isn't it?'

(Why do I ask that? I just *hope* what I've got is worst.)

'Well...' Aunt Laura begins.

I say quickly: 'It's Dad's fault. He's the one who crashed.'

'But not on purpose, my sweet. No one does these things on purpose.'

I try not to think any more. But thoughts keep coming: it's Dad's fault and Mum is all by herself, in a hospital that is much too big and much too far away.

I'm taken to a different department.

They have to do something to my arm and a nurse says: 'This will hurt a bit.'

It does. But other things are more important.

They bring a special bed, because my arm has to be hung from a frame: a traction. Uncle John helps; he is so clever.

What a stupid thing! I can hardly move, and I'm not allowed to, otherwise my arm won't heal.

Just so long as Mum gets better.

People look so... so strange. I'm being quite normal – on the outside – but I'm afraid to look at them.

Mum was so pretty tonight, with her new cardigan and lovely little boots. I hope they aren't lost. I'd like to touch the fur of the boots now. I want to touch my Mum.

A nurse has come to say that Dad was operated on. He is on a different floor – unconscious.

Gran and Grandad are allowed to see him.

And Phoebe? She is in the other ward too – it's called Intensive Care, for people who are very ill – and she is also unconscious. Luckily they can do anything in a hospital. But it's a shame they are so far away.

Where am I going to sleep?

They take me to 6 East. That's the children's ward, on the sixth floor.

It's still dark.

'What time is it?' I ask Aunt Laura.

'Eleven.'

'How's Phoebe?'

'She has a brain contusion.'

'Oh.'

'That's rather worse than concussion.'

'Why?'

'Her brain will be damaged for a while, so she'll have problems with ordinary things like eating and walking.'

'Is she crying?'

'No. When you're unconscious, you can't cry, and you needn't, because you don't feel anything.'

'Not even inside?'

'Well, perhaps deep down... Now, darling, you'd better have some sleep.'

'And you?'

'We are going to bed as well.'

'Is it still Leon's birthday?'

'Just about.'

'Are Elise and Rachel asleep yet?'

'No, that's why we must be going home. They're shocked too.'

'And me?'

'The loveliest nurses are going to stay with you. Like Janet... They will be here all night, so you can sleep soundly.'

'No, I'm frightened. I'll dream about the accident, and...'

About Mum, I want to say, but I don't.

'Do try,' Gran says. 'You're so tired... And you can always ring the bell. The nurse will come right away. Are you comfy now?"

I'm on my back, because my arm is held so high. Anyhow, I'm not tired. I want them to stay here all night, but they've already put their coats on.

'Goodnight, sweetheart,' says Aunt Laura. 'You are doing very well.'

'Goodnight. What a crazy birthday. Will you say hello to Leon and Rachel and Elise?'

They all kiss me.

I'm not crying, but as soon as they are gone, I press the bell and tell Janet I'm not going to sleep. I tell her I have a seventeen-year-old brother. If only that were true.

They give me a sleeping pill. But I keep waking up. Is it still night? Why does it last so long?

My face is aching. They want to give me a pill for that too, but I don't want one.

Can Mum press a bell? I'm afraid to think of her. I suppose the night is even longer there, because she is more lonely. If only I could say something to her, or even whisper... That would be all right.

Dear Mum...

Janet gives me some tapes to listen to and I'm so pleased. At least I don't have to think any more.

Monday, December 14th

I T'S SO LONG till morning...

'What time is it?' I ask again. And: 'When is Phoebe coming to stay in my room?'

There are other nurses, who ask lots of questions too, about school and things. Just so long as they don't ask anything about the accident.

My friends are going to school now. How will they know I'm here? When are we going home?

'Is Phoebe awake yet?' I ask.

'I don't think so,' says the nurse.

'Why?'

'Because she is unconscious.'

'Can I see her?'

'No, I'm sorry. She is too ill.'

'And Dad?'

'He hasn't come round yet either.'

All of a sudden Jack is here! It's still dark: only eight o'clock.

Jack and Trish are friends of Mum and Dad, and they live almost next door.

'Hello! We had an accident!'

'Yes,' says Jack, 'that's why I've come. To read to you.'

'Shouldn't you go to work?'

'Yes, I should. But right now this is more important.'

He sits down, with a very thick book, and starts at page one. Reading is the best thing there is. Mum has read a hundred books to me.

Now it gets light quickly.

The nurses come and check and feel all kinds of things. I must eat and drink – difficult – and pee lying on my back – more difficult. And Jack goes on reading all morning, till Gran and Grandad are here again, with Uncle Ernest and Aunt Nicky. Have they travelled all this way for me? Or...

I want to hug them – with one arm. It's like a party, but...

I am afraid to look at them. I don't know what to do when people have tears in their eyes.

Gran and Grandad have brought my dolls.

'How did you get these?'

'From home,' Gran says.

'Home?'

'Jack and Trish have a key.'

'Is it empty and cold now, in our house?'

'Yes. Very empty.'

'Are you going to see Mum too?'

'Yes, but first Dad and Phoebe.'

'Who's with Mum then?'

'Gran and Grandad Anderson, and Aunt Judy. Extra special care is being taken of her. There is always a nurse with her. But she can't have many visitors.'

'Why not?'

'She is so ill that the room must be kept very quiet.'

'Can she talk now?' I ask.

I know it's a dumb question, still...

'Mum was operated on last night,' says Grandad.

'In the night?'

'Because she was so badly injured. And now she'll be unconscious for a long while.'

'Why?'

'To have a long and deep rest.'

And to be better? I want to ask, but I don't.

Can you get better when you've been unconscious for so long?

Aunt Nicky stays with me. She goes on reading when the others leave to see Dad and Phoebe.

So we're in this hospital together and we can't even see each other.

Someone comes to dress the wounds on my face, and to say that I should drink something, but I don't want to.

I ask Annet if I can go home next Saturday. Annet is the activity leader, so she has no idea when I'm going home, but I ask her all the same.

There's no one at home, of course, but Gran and Grandad will stay with me there. Or I'll sleep at Karen's and Rianne's. They are my friends next door. They are fourteen and fifteen and could help me get the house ready for when Mum comes home: tidy up, put flowers in vases, do the most beautiful drawing, go shopping, buy cakes, make coffee...

I'll never moan again or make a mess of things.

If I could go and see Mum, I'd tell her that. Even if she can't talk. I bet she would hear me.

How stupid that she's so far away in Denton. She could easily stay in my room here. I can be very quiet, and careful, and I'd make sure that visitors were quiet too.

'Dad was awake for a moment,' says Gran when they come back.

'What did he say?'

'He can't talk yet,' says Grandad. 'He is on a breathing machine.'

'Breathing machine?'

'Yes, his lungs have collapsed, so he can't breathe by himself. There are special machines for that.'

'It's so clever,' says Uncle Ernest. 'There is just a tube in his mouth, and the machine does the rest.'

'We talked to him,' Gran says. 'We told him that you are in such a grand room and that all these dear people are coming to see you. I held his hand and said: "Press when you hear me," and he pressed it pretty hard.'

'What else has he got?' I ask.

'A broken leg, broken ribs and concussion. But you know what's odd? He looks very strong.'

'Strong?'

'Yes, isn't that strange? He is on his back, with his eyes closed, and yet he has this strength about him. The nurses see it too. Dad will soon be better.'

'And Phoebe?'

Gran swallows. I can't help seeing it, I see everything. Some light disappears from her eyes. Gran has these huge eyes with a lot of light in them, so it's easy to see.

'Phoebe is all right, but she looks small and weak.'

'Sad?' I ask.

'Yes, she is having a hard time.'

'Have you talked with her too?'

'We told her that Dad and you are nearby, that sort of thing, and I think she heard us.'

'Did she also press your hand?'

'No, she can't.'

They are leaving again. There are things I want to ask about Mum and school, but they have an appointment with the police, to talk about the accident, and at home they will be busy as well, because everybody is calling them to ask how we are and to offer help...

I must eat.

Visitors are great, but they always leave.

After lunch I must sleep. Then it's terribly silent here. By accident I really fall asleep.

After that a lot of people arrive; some of them also go to see Dad and Phoebe.

Miss May has come from school and I tell her: 'Dad was making jokes and then he looked over his shoulder. Mum said: "Never do that again."'

'This often happens in cars,' Miss May says.

But an accident doesn't.

There is no news about Mum. She is in a coma and that might take a long time. Coma means that you are nearly dead. But you *can* get well. In a hospital they can do almost anything. Some people die though. Of cancer and things. Or in an accident. Especially a serious accident like ours.

There isn't much news about Phoebe either. She's got tubes for food and oxygen and medicines.

The news about Dad is always good: 'He can write!'

First with his finger, letter by letter on his chest, then with pen and paper, but topsy-turvy.

In this way he asks all kinds of questions, about Mum, Phoebe and me, and even about our rabbits!

Oh no, I forgot! Who's looking after Pete and Gerry? They need fresh water every day and food twice a day. We often let them have a good run in our room and their hutches must be cleaned – a lousy chore.

Soon enough I find out that Karen and Rianne are taking care of that, with their father and mother. Karen is really afraid to hold them, but she does.

With all these visitors it's easier to eat something. But with more people coming, more will be leaving, and what about after supper, when it's dark again?

What shall I do now? My mind is a jumble, the bandage round by arm is too tight, my legs want to run...

I want to see Mum and Phoebe. I'd like to watch them sleep and see why everyone has frightened eyes when they talk about them. Just when I'm about to ring the bell again, Jack comes in, with his nice thick book.

Bedtime means reading. Does he know that Mum always reads to me? Mum and I often drive each other crazy at the library. I can never make up my mind about which books to choose. There are so many! So Mum wants to choose them for me, which makes it even worse! And when she goes without me, she brings the perfect books – count on that.

Trish is now putting Brian to bed, and then Donovan and Muriel. They have been my friends ever since I can remember. When I'm home again, I'll go and play with them all day.

'Were they shocked?' I ask Jack.

Of course, that's normal. Still. I want to ask. I can't believe that we've had such an accident. That Mum is in a coma...

Nobody is putting me to bed: I *live* in bed. I needn't even undress. The nurse wants me to brush my teeth though. Then we have a last chat and the light is switched off.

Tuesday, December 15th

WHEN I WAKE UP, is it still night? I'm lying at a funny angle. They give me a glass of hot milk. My arm is cold. I listen to some tapes again – it is still night – and I get a pill.

Another day has begun just like that. Everyone is going to school, except Karen and Rianne, and Elise and Rachel. They didn't go yesterday either, with the shock, and with grief.

Grief? Why am I saying that? Because I feel it. And see it. I just can't help it. Nobody can; it's there, hanging around us. Sometimes it takes hold of me, and I grow cold. Then I ring for a nurse.

Jack drops by very early again. Normally, only parents are allowed in at any time. But today he's on his way to work.

He works in Denton.

Are you going to see Mum too? I'd like to ask. *Tell her…*

What would I tell her?

Dear Mum…

There is much too much to say.

Now it's just as if I become deaf and blind.

I don't want to talk to you, I want to nestle softly and quietly and feel and smell you. You smell so… so like Mum.

Fortunately Gran and Grandad come. Then Uncle Alex and Aunt Phyllis, Trish, Annicka and many others, more or less taking turns… And they all bring presents or sweets. I get cuddly bears, cards, books, games, tapes, letters… The nurses are worrying about all these visitors but for now they are allowed in.

They read to me, rub my cold feet, study the traction, and we chat about all sorts of things – very cosy. The nurses hardly get to see me.

So on the outside everything seems normal. But some people see my inside. If that opens a little, it really hurts.

Wednesday, December 16th

My ROOM is decorated, especially the traction, with balloons and all the cards made by my whole class.

When Annet and the others are so busy, I forget why I'm here and why I still haven't seen my father, mother and sister.

Annet has been to see Phoebe.

'What did she say?'

'She is still very sleepy. She just mumbles in her sleep.'

'What does she mumble?'

'It sounds like, "No, no!"'

'Is she angry then?'

'Well, it sounds like it, doesn't it?'

Me too, I'd like to say.

'I want to see her too,' I say.

'Not yet. Perhaps she will come soon and be in your room. But you know, your Dad is awake now; you can see him for a few minutes.'

I want to get up right away. But of course I can't.

'Wait,' says Annet, 'we're coming with you. We'll steer you in your bed.'

This is fun: out of the room, along the corridor, into the lift, along another corridor... A bit scary too. It makes me feel sick. The accident seems years ago. And minutes ago. What will Dad look like?

First I see all these machines with tubes. Then my own real Dad. With a tube in his nose and on his arm. His eyes are closed. He does not look strong at all! How still he is.

'Hi, Dad!' I call.

His eyes open but his body doesn't move, just his head, enough to look at me.

'Dad will never make jokes again,' he says.

As if he has skipped a few days.

Janet says: 'We'll be back. See you, Rosemyn.'

Dad is lying on his back and can only turn his head. We can't hug each other or hold hands.

'What have you got on your forehead?' I ask him.

'A wound. Ugly?'

He talks very softly, as if each word hurts.

'Why are you whispering?' I ask.

'My lungs don't work very well yet. I can't get much air.'

There is blood on his head.

'Does that hurt?' I ask.

'Nah... How are *you*?'

'All right. I got lots of presents. Will Mum get better?'

'I don't know.'

'What do you think?'

'I really don't know.'

'But what do you *think*?'

'Sweetie, Mum's body is badly injured. I don't know if she *can* get better.'

'What has she got?'

'Very serious concussion and in her stomach things have got broken.'

I've heard it often enough, but I still keep on asking – because I don't want to believe it.

Now I get this funny feeling again: my inside knows more than I want to. Better talk about something else.

'I've watched TV.'

'In hospital? Is that good for children who are ill?'

When he tries to look at me, his head keeps falling back. Janet has come for me already.

When can I come again? I want to ask, and *When are we going home?* and much more about Mum and Phoebe…

But we're rolling along the corridors again.

It's strange to come back to my room. It seems like coming home. It *seems*.

Home is the best thing there is.

I keep thinking that there is nobody there. And that the telephone might ring. Does the house miss us when the phone rings?

Trish went to see if there was any food that might go bad. Dad had been to the market and bought piles of fruit – for the vitamins. The fridge was full, with milk and cheese and things. And a cake! What was that for?

Mum often makes cakes. She always thinks of something to celebrate. Or just because we're sad. Or to make up for a row.

My favourite job is kneading and rolling (and tasting) the pastry for cakes and biscuits. My *very* favourite job is cutting out the shapes of the biscuits, like hearts or stars…

Mum says I've got perfect hands for kneading, because if they are too warm, it goes all wrong.

Sometimes I can make a butter cake by myself. Other times, when it doesn't work, Mum gets stressed.

What shall we buy when we come home? We'll deserve something very special.

Lunch is brought. But I don't need anything. They do their best to make me eat and drink, but I don't want to.

People are still coming all day, even from my old street and my old school, although we moved a long time ago, and it's crazy: as if I'm everywhere at the same time.

Some people have come cycling from far away and then the outdoors smell is still on them, especially when it's raining – I can taste it on their cheeks.

Some are shy – kind of cheerful and scared at the same time – when they have been to see Phoebe.

I want to see Dad again but he's too tired. He has to learn to breathe deeply all over again and he sleeps for the rest of the day.

Mum's friend Trudy has come for a bedtime chat and that's an extra comfort because she has been through something hard too: her little Hannah died when she was seven.

Why am I saying this? None of us has died! Still, I

want to hear everything about it, also what I already know, about the funeral and things.

Meanwhile Trudy rubs my feet, with a soft cream that makes me feel lovely and warm.

Thursday, December 17th

I SLEPT QUITE WELL, but since I'm always in bed, there is not much difference between day and night, which is both good and annoying.

At bedtime at home I always make a fuss. I hate brushing my teeth, I hate going *to* bed and getting *out* of bed. (I wish I could now…) And Mum is such a fogey about watching TV! There are so many programmes I like but she says they make me edgy or overactive or addicted… She's afraid I'll stop reading and painting.

My arm is hurting pretty badly now. The nurse says it's swollen. The bandage is too tight, that's for sure.

During the night I often wake up because my body is all wrong.

At last, Phoebe has come to stay in my room! I want to hug her and ask a thousand questions – I'm sick with happiness – but she doesn't do anything, can't do anything, just lies there, sleeping and crying. She doesn't even know where she is and that I'm right beside her.

If only I could get out of bed! I'd stroke her softly and give her little kisses.

She has rolled herself up like a baby. She is six but

seems to have shrunk – just like a fairy, with that light, gleaming hair of hers.

'Phoebe?'

No answer.

'Phoebe!' (Much louder.)

Moan.

'Shall I read to you?'

No answer.

She is still a bit unconscious. But perhaps she can hear me a little as well. Deep inside?

I can't get a book myself. Shall I ring? No, what if they won't let me... I'll think of something.

'One day...'

And I tell her the best stories I can remember.

But Phoebe doesn't react at all, only with moaning or even screaming.

'What's wrong?' I keep asking.

She doesn't look or move.

And now I don't feel like eating again.

Phoebe gets food through the tube in her nose that runs all the way to her stomach.

In her tiny little arm is a smaller tube, a permanent drip for fluids and medicines.

I want to know everything and the nurses explain.

Our visitors must pass Phoebe's bed first (she is near the door) and they do that very quietly. I've stopped being quiet; she doesn't notice anyhow. And at times that makes me so nervous that I become even noisier and make the nurses angry. Not on purpose, mind.

With Aunt Laura and my cousins I go to the playroom. They like wheeling my bed, and I like it too.

This afternoon I'm going to see Dad again. He's been moved to 5 West.

Our beds are put very close, but Dad is still too ill to move. He looks even more tired than yesterday.

Again I ask about Mum. Again these useless answers. Nobody says when she will be better. Just as if nothing is happening! Yes, that's the worst feeling: that there is no news.

Dad has to do something horrible. In his lungs there is still some mucus, which he must cough up until it comes out of his mouth like a ball. Coughing is impossible, with broken ribs, but he must. Or else he will get pneumonia.

When Dad says it's time for me to leave again, I start talking very quickly, because I don't want to leave so soon. Even if he can't do much, I want to be with him so desperately. But he's got a bell too and the nurses come at once.

'Bye, Dad. When can I come again?'

'Oh darling, I don't know. As soon as possible, all right?'

'All right. Tonight?'

'I hope so.'

'OK, see you tonight!'

(Sometimes I think: what I *say*, will actually happen.)

Phoebe begins to talk a little, when she is asked something, but she says the craziest things. Then I laugh – I love crazy things – although it's sad.

'Do you know who I am?' Karen asks her.

'Laura and Mary,' Phoebe says. Then suddenly: 'You are sweet,' and: 'Christmas tree.'

A minute later she does something very dangerous: she starts pulling at the tube in her nose. It looks funny: like a baby that doesn't know what she's doing.

'Don't!' I shout.

It's out already. And it must be pushed back, into this tiny nose of hers.

She cries and struggles. They tie her hands to stop her doing it again.

Come on, Phe, I'd like to call.

A woman has come to play the lyre. Her name is Anna and her lyre is like a magic instrument; the sounds are so beautiful – as if an angel is playing. It makes me warm and quiet. And I think Phoebe is listening too, although she has turned her back towards Anna.

What a shame it's over so soon.

'Are you coming tomorrow?' I ask.

'I hope so,' she says.

Tonight Phoebe is crying again and that makes me cry as well. She doesn't hear me, doesn't talk to me, our beds are far apart, I can't do anything for her.

And my arm is all swollen. Another x-ray will be taken tomorrow.

Phoebe is wheeled to another room; she's keeping me awake. *Never mind*, I'm about to say, I can't sleep anyway, but she's gone. She can't protest.

Oh Mum, if only you could help for a moment, with your miracle hands.

When I close my eyes, I can see you so well that it seems you're here. Come and lie beside me. All the pain goes away. Please stay with us, please!

Friday, December 18th

IN THE MIDDLE OF THE NIGHT, I wake up with the pain in my arm. In the distance Phoebe is crying.

I get half a pill and fall asleep again, more or less.

Phoebe is back in our room and seems to be awake, but she doesn't understand where she is. All drowsy, she is gazing in front of her.

We are both washed on our beds and Phoebe starts crying again. The doctor says she may lie on one pillow and when the nurses are there, her hands may be untied. But she's already asleep.

I can't see Dad today. He's had a bad night and doesn't feel well. Gran explains that he is trying to breathe without the oxygen tube. He can do it but he's too tired even to eat and drink.

So it's a gloomy day. Between visitors, I doze off too. I don't feel like eating and drinking or playing. Only reading, or rather, listening.

Fortunately there are visitors nearly all day. But my friends can't come yet. Miss May says the whole class would like to see me.

Annet tries to read to Phoebe as well and I think she likes it.

My elbow is hurting like anything! There are plasters that cut into my skin.

I'm so worried about Phoebe: she's not getting better but worse! Is *everybody* getting worse now? And no one knows when I can go home.

When Leon is here, I say once more: 'Do *you* know how Mum is?'

But he really hasn't heard any more than the others – he is the most honest person I know.

Phoebe is allowed some custard and apple sauce. She tastes the apple sauce and says she doesn't like it. Quickly I tell the nurse that she doesn't eat that at home either.

She won't let her teeth be brushed; she keeps her mouth shut tight.

Luckily her hands are left free.

Our old neighbour, Annicka, comes in and sits down with Phoebe. When her sheets have to be changed, Annicka says: 'Give her to me.'

Then Phe is in Annicka's arms. She goes all quiet and I see her thinking: This feels like Mum.

I feel jealous, so I want to talk to Annicka, but she looks at me so deeply that I say nothing.

Nurse Janny puts ointment on my face – nice.

After supper Trudy comes to read to us again.

'Do you often go to Hannah's grave?' I ask.

'Yes,' Trudy says. 'We've turned it into a little garden and I enjoy looking after it and seeing which flowers are blooming. It's lovely and quiet there.'

'What do you do on Hannah's birthday?'

'First we go to the cemetery, with flowers. Then the four of us go to some favourite place, in the country or to a museum…'

Trudy stays longer than an hour – it's already night. Phoebe is asleep.

I forget where we are till Trudy tiptoes away.

I have not asked about Mum. I don't dare any more.

Saturday, December 19th

At FIRST, Phoebe is still crying and screaming in her sleep. At six o'clock they give her some food through the tube and now she is calm.

'Phe?'

She looks at me but doesn't say anything.

'Shall I sing to you?'

She smiles and that's the sweetest thing I've ever seen. I sing a few songs I happen to think of, about summer and winter, and about Christmas.

They are going to take me to Dad and I can't wait! After a day like yesterday it seems we haven't seen each other for weeks. Surely *he* knows how Mum is.

They wheel my bed in, next to Dad's.

'Hey,' I say, 'have you got a telephone?'

Stupid question, but I'm so nervous.

'Yes,' he says, '*very* useful.'

Have you called Denton yet? I should be asking.

I look around and think of all kinds of things, as if I'm dizzy, as if I'm floating everywhere at the same time... *What* are we saying?

Suddenly I hear Dad's voice: 'Mum is not going to

get better. She is going to die. She will go back to heaven, to the light.'

From very far away I fall back into my bed, beside Dad, who looks horribly tired.

Mum is going to die.

He has said it.

My mother?

Not on television, not in a book. Our own, real Mum will never come home again.

What about us?

'No! Mum is not going to die! I don't *want* her to. And you can never be sure. Then why did you cause the accident?'

'I didn't. I mean, not on purpose. An accident *happens*.'

'Mum doesn't want to die either, because if she did we wouldn't have a mother.'

'Yes, for your sake Mum doesn't want to die. Perhaps that's why it's taking so long. But her body is all broken...'

'What's wrong with her then?'

'Her brain is partly dead already. If she were to live, she might not be able to walk, or talk. She must continue on her way and that way is now leading to heaven. Which is really a good thing for her.'

'But not for us.'

'No. For us it's hard. And Mum *knows* it. That's terrible for her as well.'

'So you don't know for sure that she is going to die.'

'No, I *think* so. We must wait and get strong. And inside you can always talk with Mum.'

It is never certain. Miracles happen, don't they? But...

Now I know what I've seen in all those eyes. I knew it from the beginning!

We are both crying.

I can't crawl into Dad's lap and we can't lean against each other.

Holding my hand, he tries to get that pretty box of tissues and give it to me. He can't, the box is too far away, on his night table, but he does it all the same!

After that he collapses again. It hurt too much. Still, I suddenly think he's strong, like Gran said the other day. He's so quiet, I mean... not just because he's tired.

I'm even relieved. At least he has said it! Although I don't want to believe what I know.

Uncle Alex and Aunt Phyllis take me back again. They are silent and sweet and stay so close that I can hold them. I can cry and talk as much as I want to. And be angry.

I've always known, or else Mum wouldn't have been left alone in Denton. Mum is going to the light and I'm glad for her, because she won't be in pain any more, but in a kind of way I'm also jealous – I'd like to go with her, so that my sadness would be over. Although... I'd miss Dad and Phe, wouldn't I...

When the nurses are there, I try to be strong, but that doesn't work. I'm so afraid of being left behind, without

Mum, even if Dad will look after us, working at home.

They put Phe's bed beside mine, for a moment. That helps.

I think it's sad that she doesn't know about Mum. Or does she?

It's lunchtime but they leave me alone.

What am I going to do if I never see Mum again?

Phoebe refuses the porridge they try to give her. She does drink some water. And nurse Renata does her best to brush Phe's teeth.

She has a support in bed, to sit more straight. How I'd like to sit up too.

Sometimes I talk about Mum without lowering my voice. What can Phoebe hear? All of it, I think. And what does she understand? That Mum is dying? Oh no, that would be too sad. Mean, even. But I can't whisper all day, can I? Besides, she would know we have a secret. If only I could just *talk* with her.

It seems she isn't my sister any more, as if she is not really alive. Will she be all right or is her brain a bit dead too? Perhaps she'll be this tiny fairy for ever, with her smile and her mouse-voice, and I won't be able to do anything for her.

Will she like my tapes? I get the Musical Hits and put them on really loud – to be on the safe side.

Tonight I eat something but Phoebe doesn't even try.

'She needn't,' I tell Janny, 'because she gets food through her tube.'

I want to do *something* for Phe. I know it's important she learns to eat again, but if it truly makes her sick?

Suddenly Janny comes to say that I can go and see Dad again.

'He was on the phone,' she says, 'because you were so unhappy.'

Now I cry with relief. I was so scared of the evening.

Dad is feeling better.

'Something was wrong with the drip for the pain. That's been sorted out and I've also eaten again.'

'Me too!'

We are both cheerful. I think because we did the most difficult part this morning.

'What's that thing?' I ask.

On the floor is a plastic bag with brownish water, on a tube hanging from his bed.

'A catheter,' says Dad. 'It's my urine. The tube takes it straight from my penis into the bag, because I can't pee lying on my back.'

'I can. On the pot.'

'You're a genius.'

'Doesn't it hurt, that tube?'

'Just a funny feeling.'

'Phoebe is wearing nappies,' I say, 'or else she would pee in bed.'

That makes me laugh. Then I cry again. Sometimes I forget that Mum is dying.

Dad says slowly: 'Mum is really with the angels already.'

'No! She's in Denton!'

'That's her body, her outside. Mum herself is often far away now. Just as if she's trying to go to heaven but also wants to stay with us.'

'But she doesn't *know* anything, does she?'

'Well, when you're in a coma, your soul is mostly out of your body and you know all the more! Like in your sleep, in dreams, you're everywhere, aren't you?'

I must think but I don't want to. He's right, I suppose, but dead is dead, to us.

All of a sudden I know what he means, just like when I feel more than I know. And the deeper inside, the more important it is. That has to do with heaven, Mum always says. It's not in the air or anything, but in ourselves, no matter if you're dead or alive...

'Mum mustn't think of us,' I say. 'Can't we do anything for *her*?'

'Yes, we can: take good care of each other and, especially, not be afraid. Mum is receiving so much strength and help that she's passing some of it on to us, when we're fast asleep, or when we're thinking of her and feel close to her.'

'She mustn't!' I shout. 'She must keep it all to herself, because she needs it more!'

I feel strong but when it's time to go back to Phoebe, that disappears. With Phe I am the biggest and I'd rather be small. While at home I always want to be older than I am.

'Can I stay and sleep here?'

'Oh sweetie, you can't. I'm too ill for that. And it's much too quiet for you here; I can't talk much. With visitors, it's not convenient either... And what about Phoebe?'

I know. Off I go. It's not his fault. Only the pavement and the tree and the darkness. Although... Everybody drives in the dark. He should have watched out!

Phoebe looks up when somebody comes in and she nods goodbye when they leave – like a doll that can move.

I'm thinking of Mum and Dad, how they quarrelled sometimes. Now they won't any more, ever.

Mum and I have been cross with each other quite often... Can I still talk with her about that?

Bill and Erica are here – a father and a mother together. We used to live next door. Bill is good at rubbing my feet, which are *always* cold as ice, while Erica reads to me or sits with Phoebe. And I ask about their little boys. If only they could have come too.

They bring us a round Unicef puzzle. We always do puzzles on the carpet in our living room. It's such fun, all of us on the floor.

Suddenly there is a terrible mess in Phe's bed. She throws up and the tube comes out through her mouth. But it was in her nose, wasn't it? We just stare at this little bundle of misery. I *told* them she mustn't eat!

They don't give her a new one – thank God.

Janny quickly brushes her teeth, which she doesn't like, of course, then she falls asleep right away.

Bill and Erica have left; it's bedtime for the boys. So their father and mother are both coming home.

In my whole life I have never felt more alone. I don't want to feel anything any more. But I must look after Phoebe.

It's quiet and dark again. There is a light in the corridor and I can see a nurse – so different from home.

When Mum dies, we'll never come home together again. We won't go shopping, or make dolls, or paint in the woods, find autumn leaves and make pretty things with them…

Is Dad asleep yet? At home he's always tired too, or writing, deep in thought in his study, or leaving…

I must see him, I can't stand it any more.

Janny comes and says: 'Shall we call him?'

Oh, yes, he's got a telephone.

She calls from the office and I can go!

We're off again, by bed, carefully past Phoebe. She's never been to see Dad. She doesn't even know we had an accident.

In his room the curtains are drawn too. The windowsill is full of flowers and postcards and a fruitbasket. There's a light in a glass tulip.

'Pretty,' I say.

'It's a present from Anne Mary.'

He's still whispering but I'm not afraid to look at him. He is sitting a little straighter and can look back at me much better.

Although he's even more tired than he was earlier today, it seems different. He looks kind of new.

'It's not fair, is it,' he says, 'that you can only stay such a short while.'

That makes me cry again.

He doesn't say *Quiet* or *Be a big girl*. He strokes my hand. Now it doesn't matter if I cry, because it's about something that matters terribly.

Once again it's time to leave and I say: 'You can sleep in our room, if you like.'

'That's very kind of your nurses,' Dad says, 'but sometimes I need to be alone. There is a lot of arranging to be done. I couldn't manage without a telephone. And my body needs rest and treatment... It's hard for me too, that we're not together. As long as we hold on, OK?'

I suck my thumb, to think about it.

'OK.'

Actually I want to ask about everything all over again, but never mind.

'Are you here for the night?' I ask Janny.

'No, there will be another nurse, otherwise the

hours would be too long. Just ring when you want to talk to someone.'

'Could I have a photo of Mum?'

'I'm sure you can, what a good idea. I'll leave a note for the nurse who is on duty in the morning. Sleep well.'

Sunday, December 20th

AT TWO O'CLOCK in the night I wake up (in the corridor is a clock I can just see) and Nurse Gwen comes.

'You know who is to blame for the accident?' I say. 'The people who didn't paint the pavement white. So it's not Dad's fault. The police said so. That pavement is just as grey as the road.'

Gwen is silent.

'We *can* live, the three of us,' I say. 'And I want to go to Mum's funeral. But inside I feel she'll get better.'

One moment I think this, the other moment that… It's almost driving me crazy. Sometimes it seems I feel everything at the same time: dying and getting better. Anyway, dying must be a kind of getting better, because you don't feel pain any more and you start all over again: no problems or anything. Then I ought to *hope* Mum will soon die. I couldn't do that, could I?

If heaven is inside us all, well, it's quite hidden all right. Better sleep first. At least that *feels* like dying.

At six o'clock Phoebe is awake (so am I). Gwen tries to give her some apple sauce and tea, but she doesn't want anything. So the tube is put back in again. How long can this go on?

When they want to make Phoebe's bed, they put her in with me for a moment. It's strange though, because she doesn't say anything, doesn't *do* anything. Still, I'm awfully glad, and so is Phe, I think.

We have chips! Because it's Sunday. *Now* I'm hungry, the nurses grumble. And what happens? Phoebe eats a few too. It's so funny to watch. Carefully she takes one chip, as if she thinks: What's this? Then it slowly disappears into that baby mouth of hers. I bet she doesn't understand it at all. She falls asleep again.

Aunt Laura, Uncle Alex and Aunt Phyllis have been to our house, to fetch photos of Mum.

'Mum has just put them all in albums,' I say. 'She was busy for a whole week!'

'Do you know what's odd,' says Aunt Laura. 'Three photos were loose in a little folder, as if they were waiting. Look…'

Yes, I know them. We go through the albums so often.

There is one photo of Mum with Phe and me on her lap (close and cosy), one of Mum and Phe in a field of flowers, and in the third photo I'm on Mum's lap in front of the yellow roses in the garden. That was in the middle of summer; Mum is wearing her sunhat.

Is it really true that we'll never be able to crawl onto her lap again? That she'll never come and pick flowers or sit with us in the sunshine? It can't be! It shouldn't be! We've only lived near the fields for one year, only one summer, and Mum loved it so much...

At last we've got a garden, where we planted a hundred bulbs, just before the accident: crocuses, daffodils, snowdrops, hyacinths...

I don't want a spring without Mum! She'd miss it so much herself.

The photos have been put in new frames.

'These frames were on Dad's desk,' says Aunt Phyllis. 'Just like that!'

'Yes, they were a present from Mum.'

And now she's in them herself.

Uncle Alex hangs them on the wall, between our beds. Phoebe doesn't see them – a good thing.

This afternoon, Uncle Alex and Aunt Phyllis take me to see Dad. He gives me a big surprise: he's out of bed and sitting on a chair!

'Smart eh?' he says. 'I've washed myself a bit and the stitches in my chest are out.'

What a pity I can't give him a hug. But at least we can *look* at each other now.

Dad has grown thin. And he hasn't shaved for a week. His hair is a mess and he keeps shutting his eyes.

'We'll ring the bell,' he says to Alex and Phyllis.

They are going to have coffee.

There is no bad news, like yesterday. Basically there is no news at all, which is not good either.

'We've had chips,' I say.

Dad is glad but also worried: 'Is that good for Phoebe?'

I tell him that Gran and Grandad Anderson came to see us. They go to see Mum every day. Gran needed to cry but she didn't show it.

'You know,' Dad says, 'I'll soon be able to sit in a wheelchair and then I'll come and see you myself. But now I'd better go back to bed.'

I hope I'll be allowed to stay after that.

'Oh dear,' Dad says.

'What's wrong?'

'The bell is on my bed!'

And his bed is on the other side of the room. And Alex and Phyllis are outside, waiting for us to ring.

'You give a yell,' he says.

I don't dare, but he can't call at all.

'Hello! Help!'

What a joke.

'Do you hear anything?'

'No.'

No footsteps, no voices. Is everybody having tea? Are there any other patients who have called?

'It's a thick door,' Dad says. 'I wonder if they can hear us in the corridor.'

I call a few more times but it doesn't help.

'I'll try to reach it myself,' he says.

He gets out of the chair, staggers, and shuffles on one foot, pulling the other one along.

'Careful, you'll fall! Can you do this with a broken leg?'

'Have to.'

His mouth becomes a line. He leans on the rail of my bed. While he's moving forward, he is suddenly stuck.

'Ouch,' he whispers.

He turns and looks back. The bag of wee has stuck behind a leg of the chair. So the tube is pulling at his penis! I feel like laughing, but I don't.

Dad stoops and puts the bag beside his feet. Holding the tube, he shuffles along, grimacing.

He can't lift his feet and sometimes he almost totters. I'm afraid to say anything and I'm afraid to look.

Dad is silent too. His eyes look far away. There is sweat on his forehead. Does it hurt? I'm in traction, I can't help, while he is shuffling right past me.

He is coming to the end of my bed and then there is an empty space. What can he cling to now? I stop looking. I hear him shuffle and pant. Except for that, there's no sound.

Then a thud. He's fallen on his bed.

'Oops,' he says. 'Just catch my breath.'

After a moment, he presses the bell.

But still nobody comes. It's taking so long!

Dad rings a few more times and then says: 'Hey, it doesn't work!'

He is staring at the light above the door – it's not on – and at the flex of the bell.

'The plug's not in,' he moans. 'My bed was moved.'

He lies down and says: 'Can't move another toe.'

All for nothing.

Then he starts laughing. And me too, of course. He

shakes with laughter and says: 'Ow, my ribs, I *can't* laugh, oh, stop!'

So that I can't stop either.

There we are: when I try to call, I get the giggles again, and when I look at Dad, holding his chest, he also starts again.

At last, the door opens.

'We were worried,' says Uncle Alex. 'But we thought you wanted to be left alone.'

After such fun, it's quiet and boring in room 647. I mean lonely.

It is evening again.

Today we had chips and all...

Phoebe looks at me but doesn't say anything. She won't eat, just sleeps and is restless at the same time. She seems to be worse.

And so is Dad. I visit him once more, but he has a temperature and is too tired to talk.

I ring about twenty times (after bedtime) and the nurse doesn't like it. But I *must* talk. She doesn't get cross, though.

At first we talk about all kinds of ordinary things, then I suddenly mention Mum. I don't want to, but it happens.

Monday, December 21st

The traction is so high now that I almost slip out of it. It makes me kick up a fuss.

Annet has been away for two days, because it was the weekend, and this morning she was shocked when she saw Phoebe, who is so terribly quiet – as if she has given up living. True: she can't understand why Mum doesn't come and if she did, it might be even worse.

As soon as Phe opens her eyes, they close again and she cowers. Is she really asleep? Or is she just waiting like a scared little bird? I suppose she thinks that Mum will be here any minute.

Annet says that Phoebe ought to see Dad. At least she would know he is still here. Annet discussed it with him and they are taking her now, by bed.

'Have a good time,' I shout. 'Say hello for me!'

Her eyes are shut tight. In the big corridor she looks even smaller. She has no idea what's happening, in the lift and things.

In the playroom I paint and play with the magnet-board. If only Mum could see what fun that is.

With Annet I also talk about Mum, but sometimes I just want to suck my thumb and think of nothing.

When Phoebe comes back, she is asleep again, so I can't even ask what it was like.

The nurses keep trying to talk to her. Then I quickly give all the answers, which makes them angry. It's important that Phoebe starts talking herself, they say. So what! Stupid nurses.

Phoebe won't eat but she licks the syrup from her fingers – because she likes being clean – and for a minute she sits on Janny's lap, just like that. Then she wants to go back to bed.

Has her visit to Dad helped already? I'd like to tell him right away, but Phoebe is taken to him again, in order to get well sooner. For the time being I can only see him once a day. And I must wait till this evening.

Luckily, most visitors come in the afternoon.

Dad tells me that Phe lay right on top of his sore places. She didn't recognize him and just moaned and squirmed against the tubes, and he couldn't move. Then she turned her back on him and slept with her head on the arm that has a drip in it.

The second time she was there, she began pulling at everything: at his wedding ring and the bedrail.

'What's this?' she asked each time.

It's sad but still we smile.

What a shame I can only see Dad once a day.

Tonight Phoebe won't look at anyone or talk to anyone. She won't eat either and after the tube feeding she throws up again.

Well, when you die, at least you've got no more pain.

Tuesday, December 22nd

Today I HAVE TO drink *six* glasses of lemonade – I promised the nurses.

Phoebe is taken for another x-ray, to see if she can have a bath. That scares me, because she's just thrown up again. That's why she can't go to see Dad this morning and I have an extra turn!

There is a funny chair in his room.

'What's that?'

'A pot-chair. Now I can pee by myself again.'

'So the tube is off?'

There is no bag on the floor.

'Just imagine,' says Dad, 'how glad I am, simply because I can pee!'

'How?'

'Well, a nurse helps me onto the chair near the wash-basin, and the wee can come of its own accord, because there's a pot hanging under the chair.'

A father on a pot!

'Then I wash sitting up,' he says.

'Are you proud?'

'Immensely. And tomorrow I'll practise walking.'

'How's Mum?' I ask.

His eyes turn dark. He wonders how honest he dares to be, I can see that.

'Mum has a fever,' he says.

'Why?'

'The doctor thinks she is bothered by the tubes.'

'Poor Mum.'

'I called the doctor, to say that we feel so bad about those machines.'

'Yes, I don't *want* Mum to be tied to machines.'

Dad sighs and says: 'There's nothing we can do. Mum can't breathe and eat by herself. But this is a very kind and good doctor, who knows what is best for her.'

I ask: 'Are you afraid Mum is going to die?'

'I *think* she's going to die.'

'And then?'

'Then I'll look after you, just like Mum did.'

'What about your work?'

'I can write at home. And we'll ask our favourite friends to help.'

I think about that. Then I say: 'Awful, isn't it, that Phoebe was sick again?'

'Yes,' Dad says, 'but I've also heard that she's going to have a bath tomorrow and that she sat on Gran's lap.'

'Just in time, because she was getting red spots all over, lying down so much. And she does answer now and then...'

'Does Anna still come to play the lyre?' Dad asks.

'Yes, almost every morning.'

'What's it like?'

'Nice. Sometimes we choose a song, like *It Came upon the Midnight Clear*...From angels bending near the earth,' I sing right away.

'Good choice,' Dad says. 'At certain moments it actually feels as if heaven is open.'

'Because Mum is going there?'

'And because we are receiving so much strength.'

Dad thinks again and says: 'As a matter of fact, we must keep heaven open ourselves.'

'Well, when Anna is playing the lyre, that's easy.'

'Soon I'll come and listen with you, when I can steer a wheelchair by myself. Are you coming again tonight?'

'Here? Whoopee! For a long time?'

'Extra long.'

'An hour?'

'Something like that... See you then.'

Annet is reading a picture book to Phoebe; she is listening quietly and looking at the pictures.

She also looks at Annet. She must be thinking: Who's this? Where *am* I?

She doesn't touch any toys, not even her own dolls.

'I've drunk six glasses of lemonade,' is the first thing I tell Dad this evening. Then I tell him everything about the day and about Phoebe, and his eyes start gleaming.

'Phe is getting better,' he says. 'This afternoon I think she recognized me and suddenly she said: "I want to go home."'

Oh no. What if Phoebe went home before me?

'But she can't eat!'

'That will improve,' Dad says. 'I explained to the nurses that Phoebe has always been a poor eater and that she's very shy.'

'Does she know that Mum isn't at home?'

'Well,' says Dad, 'it's hard to discover what she does or doesn't know, because she says so little.'

'Doesn't she ask about Mum?'

'No.'

'Or about the accident?'

'No,' says Dad. 'But I've told her that Mum will be going to heaven.'

'Out loud?'

'Yes,' says Dad.

'Because you know for sure?'

'Yes.'

I thought so.

The nurses think that Phoebe understands everything.

Dad is silent and looks in front of him. Then he says: 'Shall I tell you something beautiful? Lying against me, Phoebe fell asleep and suddenly she said: "It's all right."'

'But she was asleep!'

'Yes, she said it *in* her sleep.'

'Oh, then she was with Mum.'

'Yes,' Dad says, 'that's what it felt like.'

'But what if Mum dies?'

He hesitates. 'It will still be all right.'

He can talk calmly about Mum. Then I'm not so sad

any more. And I'm also glad that Phoebe knows, sort of.

There is a knock on the door and a man comes in.

'Hello!' says Dad to this man. 'Great!'

But *I'm* here, aren't I? My hour isn't over at all!

'Hello, Rose,' he says. 'My name is Rick Brackman. How snug you are here together.'

'Rick is from my office,' Dad says.

I wait for him to leave but Dad says: 'Do you feel like taking Rosemyn to 6 East? That would save them a job.'

'Oh, of course,' says Rick.

And Dad looks at me, to say goodbye.

'I was going to stay extra long!' I shout.

'Yes, but you've been here quite a while now and Rick has come all the way from Hammersford.'

'I'll wait,' Rick says and he makes for the door.

'No no, it's already half past six.'

I want to say lots of things – how cruel he is – but Annicka arrives too, and together they take me back: Annicka steers, Rick pushes. That's fun, and Annicka stays with me, but Dad's been mean!

Annicka lived next door for a long time. She often goes to Denton and tells Mum how we are. She is sure Mum can hear her, in her soul, because that is not injured.

'How do you *know* that Mum understands?'

'I can tell from her breathing, I can feel it holding her hands. Sometimes she swallows...'

'Don't you ever cry?'

'I do. But when I'm with her, I often feel happy and

calm – odd, isn't it? Friendship doesn't need words. Afterwards I'm sad though.'

Annicka talks about it so clearly that for a moment I seem to be with Mum myself. But soon she has to hurry home, because the boys are by themselves.

'Don't they quarrel now?'

'They *always* fight, except when I go to visit you or Mum.'

I want to ask if they were shocked, what they said, if they cried… But Annicka is really leaving. She's just as upset as I am. She also lives alone with her children. But she is not a father. I'd rather live alone with Mum than with Dad.

Another goodbye. Every evening, when it gets late, I'm so lonely that I feel cold and dark, and then the night is even more like that first one, of the accident.

Phoebe is asleep, Mum is in Denton and Dad has sent me away because of a visitor – it's not fair!

It's all right here, with the curtains drawn, but that doesn't help.

Nurse Erwin asks what's bothering me and I tell him I want to go to Dad. I'm sure Phoebe will be better tomorrow and then she will go twice.

'It's too late now,' Erwin says. 'But would you like to phone him?'

He pushes me to the office.

Dad's line is engaged.

'Let's wait,' says Erwin.

At the same time that I'm thinking that Dad could be on the phone the whole evening, *our* phone rings.

Erwin answers and says: 'Yes, Rosemyn is here.'

He hands me the receiver and Dad says: 'Your line was engaged just a minute ago!'

'Yours too,' I say.

'Yes, I was calling you!'

'And I was calling you!'

'At the very same time,' says Dad.

'Why did you call?' I ask.

'Because it was such a stupid goodbye.'

'Yes.'

'Much too quick,' he says. 'I did it all wrong, didn't I?'

I don't know what to say. I can only think of my secret: tomorrow I'll be out of traction and I'll *walk* to him. How I'd love to tell him.

'Shall we start again tomorrow?' Dad asks.

'Now!'

'No, I'm so tired I can't talk. Next time, I'll ask visitors to wait outside, OK?'

'For a long time,' I say.

'All right. Goodnight for now?'

'Goodnight.'

'How kind of Erwin to let you call. Do other children have this special treatment?'

'No.'

Other children have a father or mother who comes to see them.

'Bye, love,' Dad says. 'I'm proud of you. I think you're doing awfully well.'

'Bye.'

'Sleep tight.'
'Sleep tight.'
'See you tomorrow.'
Tomorrow I'll come walking.

It will be a great surprise, but I'm not excited. I'm nervous about the x-ray. They are going to check if everything is OK.

And what if it isn't?

My elbow hurts, because of the plaster. I don't say very often how badly it hurts – only during the night. Otherwise they'll *think* it might be wrong.

I suppose I haven't lain still enough. I keep forgetting, because I want to see everything that's going on.

Erwin stays with me for a while.

'It's much too soon for Mum to die,' I say. 'It's not fair.'

Then I want to sleep, suck my thumb, crawl away… When Mum or Dad are not with me, I want to feel nothing and know nothing.

Wednesday, December 23rd

I'M SO WORRIED about this afternoon that I can't eat or drink.

Phoebe has a slice of bread! She asked for it herself. First she pulled out the tube and they leave it out now, because she has eaten.

'What's this?' Phe asks every other minute, pointing to toys and things. She doesn't remember what toys are!

She even has a bath.

At first she loves it – I can hear exactly what's happening – but then her hair has to be washed and she hates that.

Mum does it in a special way, very slowly, with a flannel against our eyes, and with a special shampoo that doesn't make our eyes sting, and when we shout 'Stop!' she stops at once.

I'm nine, but we both hate it when all that water is running down our eyes, just as if it's coming *through* them.

Phe calls 'Stop!' and 'No, no!' but I don't think it helps. Why can't she just have fun in her bath? She's been unconscious for so long… But she had this greasy stuff on her head, for an EEG – it badly needs to be washed out.

When she comes back she is exhausted. She moves

wildly, opening and shutting her mouth. She wants to say something but she can't – something important, I think, about the hairwash. Of course she's been frightened. She's got brain damage, hasn't she? Then you're even more scared than usual.

'I need to think,' she says.

Then she falls asleep.

When Anna arrives with her lyre, Phoebe is still sleeping. But she plays for both of us and it's so beautiful that I forget everything around me, even the traction.

In the meantime our room is cleaned and Phoebe wakes up. Lying on her back, she listens quietly to the music. The softness of the sounds makes it seem we're together – I mean, as if *Mum* is here too, as if this room does not exist... Till nothing at all exists, only feeling and light.

If only it could stay like this.

When Anna stops, I'm trying to keep it that way. It works a *little*, only so deep inside that I can't reach it any more.

It *is* crazy, isn't it? Phe having a bath, as if she's almost better, although she seems only a baby, and me out of bed soon. Next thing we know I'll be walking about! On my way to Dad! I'll be able to do anything again, go home...

And by car to Mum, I'd like to think.

But I don't dare think about getting well and going home. How are we supposed to manage?

I just can't believe it. We have been here for so long now that we seem to be living here.

At lunchtime I have only a bit of soup, or else I'll feel sick. As Phoebe is so tired, I'm going to Dad now.

All the tubes are out and he's walking! Behind a kind of frame with four legs, which he leans on like a 100-year-old grandad. He is very proud but he has to be awfully careful. I'm so scared he'll fall down; he is learning to walk all over again.

'Can you stand on your wounded leg?' I ask.

'I can, but I'm afraid to. It just doesn't do what I tell it to.'

Oh no, is that going to happen to my arm?

'Dad,' I say and then I get shy.

He looks at me, waiting, so I'll have to go on.

'I have a sort of message for Mum. Shall I say it?'

He nods.

'Dear Mum, when you're going to die, please tell me, then I'll tell Dad.'

He is silent for a while and now I look at him, waiting.

'You're wonderful,' he says. 'Do you know what I just heard? Each evening hundreds of people think of Mum at the same time. She must feel something of that, don't you think?'

'Can I join in?'

'Of course.'

'What time?'

'Half past seven.'

'Shall I say my message then?'

'Yes, please. The more people who do, the more strength Mum will receive.'

'And um, can I ring you after that?'

'If the nurse agrees…'

'Oh yes, they said so.'

'OK. See you then.'

'Yes, *hear you*…'

The traction is gone. I don't recognize my own arm: it's swollen and red, with horrible sores at the elbow.

I feel big tears that don't come out. I feel pain and gladness mixed up.

I want to tell Mum about it. She always knows what I mean. So does Dad, but I've just come back from him.

And Phoebe… She can't even open one of her eyes. She did pull out the thermometer though – much too soon – and she won't let them put it back in. She's had a slice of bread and some apple juice, but now she's so tired again.

I get a different bed and can sit up a little. What a pity I can't show Dad.

I'm not allowed to walk yet, because that x-ray (to check if everything is all right) is not being taken until tomorrow. Must I stay in bed because they *think* it's still not right?

Phe is really going crazy now: everything she touches, she tears or breaks to pieces, even her dolls. And she keeps grabbing the air, as if she wants to hold it.

She only calms down when somebody reads to her.

After that she cries and tosses again. But she does go to Dad.

Now that my arm is free, I can lie any way I like, but I'm not comfortable at all and I can't sleep.

Luckily Erwin is on duty again and he lets me call Dad. That helps. I'm so nervous about tomorrow.

Thursday, December 24th

PHOEBE IS ACTING STRANGELY in her sleep and every time she wakes up, she wants me to press the bell. She's afraid of it.

They take her to another room, because she keeps waking me up, although I like pressing the bell.

In the other room they read to her, even though it's night.

Later, Phoebe eats and drinks almost normally, as if nothing had ever happened. She also plays with her dolls now and even asks for a bath.

I don't want any food.

We are going downstairs, to the x-ray department. There, an assistant lifts me out of bed in one go and puts me on a stool. Then I throw up – it isn't my fault, is it?

When we come back, Phoebe has gone to see Dad.

I can walk a little and my legs feel all new. My arm is hurting terribly though.

'Can I go home now? Or actually to Gran and Grandad, because Dad is in hospital.'

'Let's wait for the results of the x-ray,' the doctor says. 'And eat properly, get strong and practise walking…'

So once again I've asked for something I don't believe in.

Phe too keeps saying she wants to go home.

She's not wearing nappies any more; I ring if she needs to pee. She has even been to the toilet. Everybody is proud of that. And she's less scared of the corridor. Still I hope they are not taking *her* for an x-ray. Without me, she won't even go to the playroom.

I have different feelings all the time. Phoebe is getting better, and that is good and scary at the same time. This afternoon I walk about, along the corridor, to the playroom and later on I'm going to Dad… It makes me laugh to see how surprised everybody is. But something is wrong. Am I cured just like that? If my arm is OK, I have nothing serious any more, only a cut above my eye, which I pick at (and I shouldn't!). Too bad.

Completely cured? After an accident like that? Everything back to normal? It doesn't sound right. And I'm almost afraid to mention Mum at all – why?

Why don't I ask Dad to hurry to Denton this afternoon? Perhaps because my arm hurts so much.

I know what's wrong: it's just as if my arm is more important than Mum today.

Even reading doesn't help, only on the outside. I'm getting fed up with everyone and everything. I start shouting, even to kind people. And the biggest problem is that inside I'm stuck, or something. At times I don't *know* what I'm doing. So I start yelling instead of crying.

71

And that makes it even worse, because it drives the nurses mad too.

Just as I thought: the x-ray is bad news. The bone in my arm has not healed. Tonight I have to go back into traction. And my surprise for Dad? Oh, what a shame! What can I do? Shitty arm!

With a nurse I walk all the way to 5 West; my arm is in a sling. I feel as weak as anything and so miserable… But going into Dad's room, I act as if I'm glad.

'Hi, Dad!'

He is just as surprised as I expected: 'Are you out of bed?'

Now we can hug each other, making up for weeks.

'But the x-ray is bad,' I say.

'Oh sweetheart, I've heard. That's why I don't understand that you're walking!'

'They will bring another bed again, tonight. So I can walk all day and have a bath!'

'So you'll have a nice day after all.'

One nice day, what good is that?

'Come and lie here,' Dad says.

I nestle against him. Careful. What a good thing all those tubes are gone.

'Which is your bad leg again?' I ask, to be on the safe side.

'You know,' he says, 'I've practised with the walking frame and perhaps I can manage a wheelchair tomorrow!'

He's put his arm around me and I hug him as tightly as I dare.

'When will your lungs be better?' I ask. Because he is still whispering.

'Oh, they improve every day.'

'Are you less tired then?'

'Well, the trouble is that every day I must *do* more as well: wash, walk, see my daughters in turns... Shall I tell you something? This Phoebe of ours is giving me a hard time. Honestly, I couldn't even eat my cake. She grabbed it out of my hand and crammed it into her mouth, in one go.'

I laugh so hard that Dad moans: 'Ouch!'

'She wants to eat and drink anything she sees, and when she was being taken back, she fought against it.'

'How long will I be in traction this time?'

'I think another ten days. But the good thing is that we might all go home together.'

'And if not?'

'Sweetie, let's not worry about that now; we'll take one day at a time. You take care to lie still, so that your arm can heal, OK?'

'Yes,' I say.

My one single walking-day is almost over. Ten more days in traction? I can't!

I want to hide behind Dad and never come back. If Mum dies, I'd like to die too. No, that would be mean to Phoebe.

Dad is silent. Perhaps he's thinking the same thing.

To the nurse I say that Mum is going to get better. The

more often I say it, the more it feels real. At least…

Just before the traction arrives, I have a bath. It's a big, beautiful, hot bath and for a moment I forget all the things that are so horrible – as if I'm swimming in the sea, in summer…

We always go to a cottage by the sea and those are the best times of my life: with Mum and Phe on the beach. Dad too, but he is always so busy, even in the holidays, with writing and things… Most of the time he's absent-minded, except when we play in the waves.

Mum likes the same things as I do: gathering shells, gazing over the water, digging in the sand, walking through the waves… That's what everybody likes, but we do it in the same way: very quietly, very slowly, more on the inside than outside. It's got something to do with heaven and it only happens when I'm with Mum. Sometimes with Phoebe, when we are digging hard by the wild waves.

So what's to become of that…

Mum always packs our things and buys loads of sweets for the journey.

I remember how I hated swimming lessons – at first. How I begged and nagged about skipping a lesson, *just this once*, each week. Mum never gave in, even though she wasn't too keen about taking me either – at dinnertime and all… When I got my certificate, after two years, she bought me the big, soft, hairy monkey that I still have.

Will we go on holiday next summer? Can Dad do it all on his own? If only it could be just as nice.

But you're *not* dying, are you, Mum? You are the best and strongest mother in the world!

I won't mind school next time and I'll never be cross any more. Can you hear me? Have a good rest but then you must be well.

When you're almost in heaven, you can hear almost everything and you *know* everything. I'll check with Dad tomorrow.

Tomorrow is Christmas Day. Perhaps it will turn out all right.

Ann is with me in the bathroom (she is Karen and Rianne's mother) and she helps with the hairwash. The nurses are terribly busy.

Just now, when I'm in the bath, a choir has come to sing in the ward. Bad luck. I can hear it anyway – the door is open.

Phoebe goes with Rianne.

It's beautiful. I hear *Once in Royal David's City*. That's Mum's favourite carol – what a coincidence. And *It Came upon the Midnight Clear* and quite a few that I know.

At school the Christmas service was ages ago. So now the holidays have begun. Some holidays!

In the meantime I have hardly felt the hairwash. Ann is so good at it; she must have dealt with a thousand tangles.

Phoebe enjoyed the choir too, I think, but she is exhausted and falls asleep.

All of a sudden she wakes up and goes so crazy that it scares me. And I feel sorry for her. She takes all her clothes off and pees in bed.

Now she's calmed down and is eating some bread.

'Comes with brain-contusion,' says the nurse.

'Will it go away?' I ask.

'Usually, yes.'

When I go back into traction, it's late, and it doesn't work at first.

'We'll need an extra bar,' they say.

But I can't stand it any more! I don't want any traction, or bar, or hospital. Only my mother! I want everything to be normal again, with school and holidays...

I'm so frightened.

What is there to celebrate tomorrow?

Dear Mum, when you are going to die, please tell me, then I'll tell Dad.

Friday, December 25th

IT'S CHRISTMAS – in the hospital – and we have a feast of a breakfast: rolls, currant buns, a boiled egg... We both tuck in.

What's Christmas like for Mum? She doesn't even have a tree and she can't eat.

Phoebe won't take a bath. We are washed on our beds and go to the playroom together, till Dad comes, in a wheelchair. He's talked about it for days but this is real. For the first time we are together, the three of us. I mean the five of us, because Gran and Grandad have come too.

I don't know what to do with gladness. But Phe and I are in bed and we *can't* do anything.

Anyway, Dad doesn't like the playroom.

'Such loud music,' he says. 'I don't think it's good for Phoebe.'

True, she's staring blankly in front of her.

We hurry to our own room and there we have cakes and something to drink. We all say that we are spoiled and it's awfully cosy.

Dad loves our room.

'So big!' he says a few times. 'All this sunlight and the drawings and decorations!'

Then he sees Mum's photos – the sun is shining right on them. He swallows but takes a good look.

We don't talk for a moment.

Then I point to all the presents we got and to the box of sweets.

The room looks so different now, because the sun is shining – for the first time! All those days it was dark and gloomy, with a lot of rain, but today it's so light that it hurts my eyes.

'Wow,' says Dad, 'your room is facing south!'

'No,' I say, 'we're 6 East.'

'Yes, this wing itself is East, but the windows face south, so the sun will be here all day.'

In that wheelchair he's enjoying the view. We can see a long way: across fields with narrow little roads and tiny cars. The funny thing is that we can't hear anything from the outside, as if it's not real, not our world.

The sun makes me so glad that everything is fine, or *will* be fine.

'Have you got a tree?' I ask Gran and Grandad.

'Yes. Uncle Ernest brought one.'

Dad talks to the nurses about a misunderstanding: they thought I wasn't supposed to drink milk (Phoebe is allergic); then the morning is over already. Dad is tired but happy. Gran and Grandad take him back and go home themselves.

Phoebe is sleepy.

Another x-ray is taken of my arm, to see if it's hanging the right way.

At lunchtime we have chips and Phoebe eats a whole lot.

Then we have our nap and when I wake up, all I know is that I've dreamed about Mum, and that I'm frightened. That doesn't fit in with the good time we had this morning, which makes it even worse. There must be something wrong, something unexpected. It feels as if Mum has been to see me. To say goodbye...

No, I don't *want* to think that way.

But that's how it feels.

Aunt Laura is in the corridor, with Leon, Elise and Rachel. Earlier than usual? Or did I sleep longer?

They've brought a big pine branch.

'Found it in the forest,' Aunt Laura says. 'On our way here.'

I smell it – mmm. There are chocolates in it and she hangs it on the foot of my bed.

They look sad. I get this feeling again that I know more than I know. I'd like to scream: *Say* something, *do* something... But I look at the branch and think of this morning and feel the sun (a *new* sun).

My cousins live near the forest. Sometimes I forget that's where we were on the night of the accident. Aunt Laura was talking with Mum, on our way home.

We haven't been home for two weeks now.

Did I say anything to Mum then? I can't remember.

Perhaps Aunt Laura is the one Mum spoke to for the last time. They were talking about... today! Aunt Laura asked: 'What are your plans for Christmas? Do you feel like coming to us?'

Now she's here. She says: 'I'm going to see Dad for a minute.'

She is Dad's sister and whenever she's here, she goes to see him too, of course. They have lots of things to arrange and Aunt Laura helped him with scary things, like when the stitches were taken out and when he had to cough up that mucus from his lungs. So she always leaves for a while and then the five of us have fun together. But now I am terrified. It's different. Just as if Aunt Laura is going to do something special, something difficult. I know, I *know*... She looks sweet, which makes it all the harder.

Leon, Elise and Rachel have come almost every day and they make themselves at home here. They bring a book, read to us, do our hair, play games, play a tape, talk about the stables where they are so busy every day, especially in the holidays. They often win prizes and things.

But this afternoon I hate it all. They don't know I dreamed about Mum, and why... What *do* they know? The same as I do? *Say* it then!

I start yelling and calling names. Then I'm so ashamed that I creep away under the blankets. I hate everybody.

Especially Mum!

You mustn't die, you are letting me down! It's much too soon. It isn't fair. *Why* then? I'm mad at Leon – at least he's strong and alive and here – but it's really about you!

I don't want to live without you. And Phoebe... Dad is in a wheelchair, with broken ribs and an iron pin in his leg. How can he look after us?

He's coming.

'Oh my darling,' he says. 'Do you know?'

'How's Mum?'

'The doctor called. Mum's condition is so bad that they are taking her off the machines.'

'And then?'

'Then she can finally die.'

'Why!'

'Perhaps because she has a special, beautiful task in heaven. To us she's been special and she knows, I think, that we can go on. I'm glad that she can now have a rest. She'll be so free and light that we'll feel that as well, inside.'

Words, words, *words* piling up in my head. What am I supposed to *do* with them? I've stopped hearing what he says. There's only one word that remains: dead. My mother. In a moment.

My mother is going to die.

Dad's voice is soft and strong. That helps more than the words. He knows what he's talking about, I think.

Aunt Laura says: 'We are going home now and we'll

drop into Dad's room, to water the flowers.'

'Bye, Rose,' they all say. And: 'Bye, Phe.' But she is more or less asleep.

Aunt Laura says: 'I'm so glad Dad can be with you now.' She gives me a hug. They wave and are gone.

Dad stands up on one leg and tries to hold me. I feel his arm and his head – he's never been so big and close – and suddenly the anger disappears. There remains a kind of empty spot, which I'll keep for Mum, I suppose.

'How will you know when Mum has died?' I ask.

'Grandad will call. He is going to Denton, with Gran and Grandad Anderson, Aunt Judy and Mum's friends. They are taking flowers and candles, and Elizabeth will play the lyre.'

'Like Anna?'

'Yes.'

'But we can't give Mum any flowers.'

'We can,' he says. 'I asked Grandad to come and take the most beautiful ones from my room, from us. Yesterday I was given some yellow roses with an extraordinary scent – beautiful, sunny yellow. One of them was all limp, I kept it myself, and the other nine were wrapped up well against the cold, because it's freezing outside.'

'Why aren't *we* going to Denton?'

'We can't. Remember this morning was the first time I sat in a wheelchair... Also, it's more important to Mum that I'm with you. You know, I have this feeling that she couldn't die peacefully until now, until we were together again.'

'How does she know?'

'She *feels* it. In the spiritual world you can feel much more than you think.'

Yes, she often said that herself. And I've felt it myself.

'To be honest,' Dad says, 'I'm too tired to sit. I must lie down.'

'Shall I ring?'

It's done before he can say no.

Nurse Annie fetches a bed from the teenager room and puts it between Phe and me.

It's quite scary, the way Dad gets up, shuffles a bit and lies down slowly, moaning. His face is white and thin. His eyes close.

'I'm sorry,' he says. 'But I can operate my own bed with a button, to make it higher or lower.'

He's panting, lying flat on his back.

'Does it hurt?' I ask.

'Well, takes some time...'

Phoebe is awake but she doesn't even look surprised. Has she any idea why Dad is here? She smiles. Everything is fine with her.

Dad asks Annie to put a tape in the machine: the Mary Vespers. That was a concert Mum and Dad went to together. It's my favourite tape too, but I never play it here, because it makes me think of home too much.

Dad spreads his arms wide and gives us each a hand.

This way – the three of us beside each other – we listen for a while. Tears are slipping down his face. As he is holding on to us, he can't wipe them away.

When the music is finished, we are silent.

Outside and in the corridor it's silent as well. Or is it me? Again I feel I'm everywhere at the same time, or nowhere. Just as if I've lost my body. Perhaps that's why I don't cry.

Mum is everywhere too.

In spite of myself, I let go of Dad's hand to get the song sheets from the windowsill, the Christmas songs they sang yesterday.

I start on the first page. I don't know them all, but I try them and sometimes Dad whispers along.

It doesn't make any difference, does it, Mum? You know them so well yourself.

Of one song I only read the words, because I've never heard it before: *A Flower Is Springing*.

Dad hums along.

During a pause, when I can't read a long word, Phoebe says: 'Sing!'

I didn't even know she was still awake.

Just when we've sung them all, somebody says there is a phone call for Dad.

Five o'clock.

It takes Dad a long time to get into his wheelchair and much longer before he comes back. I can tell he's been crying.

'Mum has passed on,' he says.

Passed on.

He's not afraid to say 'dead', but this sounds much kinder.

She's dead, but I know what he means. Mum has passed on to something else.

What a shame we won't *see* her anymore.

I'd love to see you again.

'Is Mum happy now?'

'Yes.'

'Doesn't she miss us?'

'No, *heaven* means that missing doesn't exist. Mum has no sense of time now; to her the past is not something separate.'

'What did Grandad say?' I ask.

'Well, it appears that *everybody* felt something of heaven. They had brought a lot of flowers and stood in a circle around Mum. Candles were lit. Grandad talked to her about peace. Elizabeth played the lyre, and do you know what she chose? *A Flower Is Springing.*'

'What we've just sung?'

'Yes.'

'Then Mum definitely heard it.'

'I think so too... After that, Gran gave her a kiss and stroked her face.'

'Gran lost her daughter.'

'Yes. But Gran had a strength, or peacefulness, that had an effect on everyone.'

Dad pauses. Then he says: 'When all the tubes and machines were gone, Mum was beautiful.'

Again there is a silence.

Suddenly I say: 'We don't need my message for Mum anymore. But I've got something else. Shall I say it?'

'Of course.'

'Have you ever looked into heaven?

Perhaps if you look hard,

you will see an angel who is new –

then that is my Mum.'

'Yes,' Dad says. 'That makes me happy too. Say it again; I'll write it down.'

From the pocket of his dressing gown he takes a pen and a piece of paper.

'I'm going to read it to Phoebe,' he says.

Phe smiles and nods. She really looks glad.

I ask: 'Can I see Mum?'

Dad thinks for a long time and says: 'I hope so. I'm not sure how, but I'll ask about it.'

Then he goes back to his room.

Annie says he may stay the night, but he needs his own bed, and the telephone – otherwise he can't discuss my question either.

When he's gone, I start crying. I feel so sorry for Phoebe. She's only six. How can she understand what's happened? And what are we going to say when she is completely better? That she's lost her Mum…

I'm so glad we are still together.

Phoebe is wide awake now. She knows exactly where we are and keeps saying that she wants to go home.

'But Mum isn't at home,' I say.

I *must* explain something, or else it's even sadder.

'Oh,' she says.

She can walk to the bathroom, with a nurse, which is scary to see, because she staggers so much.

I can't sleep and get half a pill. Annie stays with me.

Dad calls, to tell us that he'll come at half past eight in the morning, to arrange our goodbye to Mum.

Saturday, December 26th

The elbow of my broken arm is bleeding. The bandage is rubbing. Nurse Mary Ann puts a piece of gauze on it.

'Mary Ann' sounds like 'Marian'. That is Mum's name. *Dear Mum…*

It's five o'clock in the morning. How long before Dad comes?

At half past eight I've been waiting for ages. I've looked at the clock a hundred times.

Dad doesn't arrive until nine and he has to see the nurses first, because they are as cross as I am.

After that he says: 'My nurses let me sleep and I needed it. Then I came right away; I haven't even washed.'

'Can I see Mum?'

'If things go all right, yes. Mum's body will be taken home, till the funeral, and I asked if she could be brought here on the way. But I don't know if it's possible.'

I need to think a while and then I tell him out of the blue that I've had hot milk with honey.

'I'll tell you something too,' he says. 'Remember the yellow roses for Mum? I kept one myself, didn't I? Aunt Laura cut it very short yesterday, because it was so limp that it seemed hopeless, and now it's fine and strong and upright. It's opening beautifully and has this gorgeous scent. The whole room is filled with it!'

Dad is delighted. I think because it has something to do with Mum.

'Good, isn't it,' he says, 'that Mum is going home for a few days.'

'Who will be with her then?'

'Everyone who wants to, in turns, for one or two hours.'

'Also in the night?'

'Yes. Remember Mum went to keep vigil with Hannah in the middle of the night?'

I nod and need to think again. I went to say goodbye in the afternoon. Hannah was so peaceful, with all her favourite things...

I'm not hungry, but the nurses want me to eat something.

Then Dad is back. He looks tired and sad.

'Is Mum here?' I ask.

'Yes, I've just been with her. But I was shocked: her body looks ugly.'

'How?'

'Her face is bluish and swollen, by the machines and this journey. It's painful to see. Are you sure you want to go?'

'Yes.'

'All right.'

He thinks for a while, turns to Phoebe and asks: 'Do you want to come with us? To say goodbye to Mum?'

She nods.

In two beds and the wheelchair we are going to 5 West.

Gran and Grandad are waiting, with Aunt Laura and two more nurses.

We arrive in a big room. There are flowers everywhere and a lot of candles. In the middle is Mum's coffin.

The sun shines deep into the room.

The nurses put us beside the coffin and say: 'We'll stay near the door.'

The coffin is too high; I can't look over the edge – my arm is in the way.

'Careful,' Dad says. But he can't help.

The nurses come back. They lift me out of traction and hold me high.

'Not ugly at all. It really is still Mum.'

She is wearing the pretty sweater she knitted herself, with the new blouse and the shell necklace.

'Can I see?' Phoebe asks.

She is lifted up too.

'Mum is asleep,' she says.

'Mum is dead,' Dad says. 'This is her dead body.'

'Why has she got blood on her mouth?' I ask.

'Because of the tube, I think.'

I stroke her face. It's cold. I can feel that she's not alive. But she's still so sweet.

When we are back in our room, Uncle Ernest and Aunt Nicky arrive and they are wearing neat, dark clothes.

We must sleep and Dad goes to his own room. The

others want to stay – for us. They will wait in the restaurant, although they aren't hungry.

Sleep? How could I sleep now! I ask the nurse to ring the restaurant.

Aunt Nicky lies down on my bed and Uncle Ernest lies beside Phoebe – like a bear with a baby.

Then I cry.

My arm is as bluish and swollen as Mum's face. Sometimes I forget the pain in my arm; at least that will get better.

With my eyes closed, Mum's face is just like it used to be again: soft and warm. She looks at me, with her big eyes, but that's hard, because they are *too* loving – then I get such a shock when I realize where I am and where we've just been.

Tonight Dad has brought his tea. How lucky it is that he's been able to come here since Mum died. I've got used to his dressing gown and the wheelchair. It seems we are living here, the three of us.

A small table is put beside my bed, for Dad and Phoebe. It's so sweet how Phe is munching at the bread in her long, pink nightie. She doesn't say anything and eats slowly, but one slice after the other disappears down her throat. After all, she's making up for two weeks.

My supper is on the bed-table and after one slice of bread, my bed is crawling with crumbs.

'When will Mum be buried?' I ask.

'Monday.'

'Are we going?'

'No, my love. I'm not up to that.'

'I am.'

'Let's take care that we get well. You mind your arm. I think Mum is happiest with that too.'

'Is she going to be buried near Hannah?'

'No, in Gorsemere.'

'Why?'

'Mum was born in Gorsemere, and that's where Gran and Grandad Anderson live.'

'But it's too far away!'

'No, it's not so bad. We often drive to Gran and Grandad, don't we? We'll pass by the cemetery. And the swimming pool is close by. When Mum was little, she lived there, she used to play at the farms, and remember the swans' nests? It's a beautiful spot. In summer we might go by bike and have a picnic. And the river runs right past our house to Gorsemere, with the gulls, the swans, the same boats...'

'Yes, I'll call: "Say hello to Mum for me!"'

But we'll never be able to walk by the water together.

'Mum is dead, isn't she?' says Phoebe.

She looks straight ahead, as if her head hurts so badly that she's afraid to move. Does she understand what she's saying? She doesn't cry. But she says: 'I want to go home.'

And again and again I want to ask *why* Mum died, but

Dad has explained so often: Mum's way now leads into heaven, so that she can have a rest and because it's Dad's turn to look after us.

Everything happens the way it has to, or else it doesn't *happen*, does it?

Dad knows what he's talking about. That's what you are a father or mother for.

He doesn't leave until Trudy comes, so we are really never alone. Trudy gives us a nice massage.

Then I feel like going to sleep.

Sunday, December 27th

WHAT A STRANGE DAY: Mum is still here and she isn't. And what is even crazier: it's almost cosy in this room.

Phoebe is walking about now. We have a Sunday lunch and a lot of visitors. I'm so glad Mum is no longer by herself in that hospital. Sometimes I feel that she is staying with me as an angel and then I don't miss her as Mum. Other times I feel black inside and I *must* be mean, even to Phoebe and especially to Dad and the nurses.

Dad has come early. Uncle Ernest is pushing the wheelchair, Aunt Nicky carries a tray full of papers, envelopes and pens, and Dad has brought his walking frame.

'What are we going to do?' I ask.

'Have coffee for a start. Any cakes and biscuits to offer us? Or have you gobbled them all?'

Ernest fetches the coffee and Dad looks in our sweets box. There aren't many left.

'What's all that?' I ask.

'Two hundred envelopes, for Mum's cards.'

Oh yes, everybody has to be told she is dead. My message about the angel will be on the cards. Dad has had it printed.

'We're writing the addresses on the envelopes,' Aunt

Nicky says. 'It's good to do that together.'

'Quite a job, mind,' says Dad, 'Because my address book is a mess.'

'But Mum gave you a new one.'

'Yes, unfortunately I haven't filled it in yet.'

'Can I help?'

'Well…'

'I could colour the envelopes.'

'*Can* you?' Dad asks. 'In bed?'

'Of course, look… here are my crayons.'

I can't write or make a real drawing, but that doesn't matter. I'll just put nice colours together.

Phoebe is doing puzzles in bed.

Dad is going through his address book and other papers. Nicky is writing and sticking on stamps. Ernest helps with the writing and looks up addresses. He goes and fetches a phone book from the nurses' office.

We're busy all morning.

'Beautiful,' Dad says, when he sees my envelopes.

I've coloured Mum's soul.

'May I have one?' he asks. 'For my card?'

'But you *know* Mum is dead.'

'Still I want to have a card of my own.'

'Me too. And one for Phoebe.'

'Of course,' he says. 'You choose the envelopes for us.'

When Grandad Anderson comes in, Phoebe's smile is as big as her whole face. She doesn't say anything but she's so glad, as if he's been lost for years. Mum looks like him. Grandad has been here before, but Phoebe was unconscious…

She goes on playing. I'm sure she is thinking: Now Mum will come any minute.

After lunch we have our nap and then we get so many visitors that the day passes quite quickly.

Phoebe is looking around; only she can't open one eye properly, and she walks like a baby, but she doesn't care.

In the afternoon Dad has been busy phoning people who have been with Mum.

'Isn't that eerie, all alone in our house?'

'No, the people I talk to tell me how pleased they are to be with Mum. Over the coffin are the big sheets she dyed yellow, remember?'

'The ones we always use to build tents…'

'They were ready in your room.'

'Yes.'

'A lot of candles are lit,' Dad goes on. 'There is always music: Mum's favourite tapes; people make coffee and tea, there are roses, daffodils, hyacinths, winter jasmine…'

'And what do they do all the time?'

'Oh, perhaps they think of moments they shared with Mum. They choose some music and keep an eye on the candles. Someone reads to her…'

'Aloud?'

'Yes. And somebody else sings. Or they tidy up and do the dishes.'

'That's silly.'

'No, love, that's part of it too. Most people like doing something practical, helping out. It's a good way of saying goodbye and they all go home with a sense of happiness.'

'Don't you feel sad you can't go?'

'Yes. But I'm so glad I'm with you. And I'm very close to Mum too.'

We get a peeled apple in nice little pieces and the nurse asks: 'What would you like to drink?'

'Ah well,' says Phoebe, 'just some crisps.'

She really doesn't get it. Yesterday she said: 'May I wake up after sleeping?'

Dad sits with her for a while.

Later he asks me: 'What would you like to give Mum to go in the coffin with her?'

'The poem about the angel. Is that all right?'

'Of course. I'll write it out again.'

'What will Phoebe give?' I ask.

We both look at her but she doesn't understand what we are talking about.

'What about the little doll with lavender, which Mum had under her pillow?'

'OK.'

'What do you think, Phoebe?'

She nods.

'And what are you giving?' I ask Dad.

'I think the rose quartz she had for her birthday.'

For a moment he looks in front of him and then asks: 'What would you say if someone read your poem at the funeral?'

I've never been to a funeral, but of course I say yes.

'Who shall we ask to read it?'

'Annicka.'

'All right. I'll call her.'

'Don't forget to write it out.'

Dad stays a little longer, lying on his bed between us.

Tonight Phoebe says she is frightened. But she doesn't know of what. Or she can't say it.

Monday, December 28th

Waking up at half past five, Phoebe says again that she is frightened. Is it something to do with Mum?

Today is the funeral.

I don't mind being washed but I won't eat or drink, although the nurses keep trying.

I quarrel about anything and start kicking and shouting!

Perhaps I feel the same thing as Phoebe. We don't *want* to behave, it's *not* a normal day.

Then why aren't we crying? Phoebe never cries. She whispers and smiles and at times she complains, like when her hair is washed, but she doesn't cry. Perhaps because she doesn't know everything yet. Or doesn't understand. She is just doing her puzzles, with those tiny hands of hers – she's so good at it. Sometimes she answers people but she hardly ever talks herself. Even when Dad comes, she goes on doing her puzzles. I don't think she's aware that Dad has come from 5 West.

He has brought his prettiest cards and the glass tulip. He puts them on my bedside table, with the roses Elise painted for us. Phoebe comes and sits in her chair and she climbs on Dad's lap, but that hurts his leg and chest.

'Has the funeral begun now?'

'All friends and the family are going to our house first, to accompany Mum to the cemetery.'

'How do they take the coffin?'

'There is a special car for that.'

He explains that Gran will say something about Mum's life and that Geraldine, a friend, will sing.

He says: 'Do you know what she suggested herself? *A Flower Is Springing*. And do you know which flower is meant in the song?'

'A rose?'

He nods and goes on after a while.

Trish wants to help carry the coffin, with my uncles and our neighbours.

Dad has to lie down again and Phoebe is put back to bed too.

It is getting very silent, because in our thoughts we are at the funeral. Does Mum know about this? Her body doesn't feel anything. So actually, we needn't have given any presents either. But what else could we do? When we were making long journeys, on holiday for example, Mum would give us presents too.

Dad keeps an eye on the clock and now and then he tells us what is happening, until Mum's coffin is lowered into the earth.

Suddenly another little poem comes up:

'I'm dead,

I'm heaven,

I'm the earth.'

Dad likes it and writes it down. Then something even stranger, which he also writes down:

'Light,
grass,
God,
water.'

I like it too and it gives me an important feeling. Just as if I must make words for what *Mum* feels, or what she now *is*.

Anyhow, it gives me a *good* feeling, even if I don't understand that.

'Now they are having coffee,' Dad says.

'At home?'

'No, there is a big room at the cemetery for that, which is nice and warm. And they really deserve it. This is often a very friendly time, you know. Because they have fulfilled a difficult task together. That makes everyone belong.'

When Dad takes the tape of the Mary Vespers, I say: 'No more crying.'

The people who come to see us after the funeral are not sad at all. They tell us how beautiful and impressive it was. Dad was right: they are glad. Not cheerful, but glad.

Aunt Nicky brings Dad's lunch from 5 West. The others find a chair or sit down on the beds, helping us with lunch – so that I finish my plateful without noticing – and telling us about this morning.

The shops were shut, but everybody brought flowers.

Our living room was so crowded that no one else could have got in.

Gran said Mum is like a ship, sailing away to sea. It gets smaller and smaller, till you can't see it any more, but it's there all right!

Uncle John shut the coffin, with our presents and some drawings in it.

When the coffin was carried outside, there was a long row of people along the path.

It is nice, frosty weather. The sun has been shining all day but I feel how cold everybody's cheeks are – like ice.

At the cemetery there were a lot more people, in a big circle around Mum's grave.

Geraldine was looking at the tops of the trees in the blue of the sky and all of a sudden she saw twelve swans flying right over the cemetery. Just like a salute for Mum.

Aunt Judy cried hard – 'On behalf of us all,' Gran says.

Then there was silence, with a lot of birds singing clearly in the frosty air.

In the coffee room all kinds of people met each other. There were even some friends from twenty years ago. After that, some of them went back to Mum's grave.

Mum is fine; everyone felt that.

They give Dad some cards that were with the flowers. On one of them it says: *Rest in peace*. And my friend Muriel wrote: *Bye, Marian*.

So *she* was at the funeral. And more children. They all loved my Mum.

What will happen now? Will they still come to our house, without Mum being there?

They've all gone home now and Dad has left for his own room. Only Phoebe and I are still here, where we are day and night. We always stay behind! And then it's so empty, especially after lunch, when it's time for our nap, and especially *this* afternoon.

At the end of the day there is a surprise. Just when Dad is back, Aunt Judy comes in with Peter and Anne Mary. They bring us chocolates and lollipops.

'Dad will be mad at me,' Aunt Judy says.

Anne Mary helps Phe with her jigsaws and I play *Who is it?* with my cousin – we have a great time.

I want them to stay for ages, but it's time for supper and Dad says we are tired.

The curtains are drawn. The sky is bright red. Beside the moon is a huge star. What a shame that Mum can't see it. Or does she see *all* the stars?

Dad says he sometimes feels lonely too, when he gets back to his room.

Last night it was cold and gloomy there, but he went to the bathroom and when he came back, somebody had lit his candles, which changed the whole room. It was Nurse Susan, who did that for Dad. When her mother died she was eleven and her sister nine – like me.

Tuesday, December 29th
and Wednesday, December 30th

IT IS HALF PAST FOUR in the morning and again I wake up with the pain in my arm. The bandage is cutting into my skin. Gwen gives me half a pill.

It's a stupid, boring day. I'm mad! Nothing is happening!
Nothing is important now that Mum is buried.

Phoebe is up and about and starts chatting away. The nurses like talking to her but I shout and meddle – I can give better answers.

When I'm alone for one minute, it seems like an hour.

At last the post comes again: cards, letters, drawings – a whole bunch. I want each nurse to read them to me, till I know them by heart. I can read myself, but this is much more fun.

Phoebe does jigsaws of forty pieces! And she knows that Mum is buried.

What *now*? When Dad comes, I have to drink water with medicine. It's the pills for my allergy and Mum used to deal with it. So I don't want that any more, ever!

Dad behaves as if things are normal and that's impossible – his own fault. He stays nice and calm all right, but I won't take a drop. I want some sweets and of course he says no. He's brought rice wafers, from home. Well, he can keep those! I won't have anything from home.

I pick at the scab on my eye and some pus comes out. And when they put a plaster on it, I fiddle with the plaster.

Suddenly Phoebe says: 'Mum is dead. What a shame.'

I take a sheet of paper and a black pencil and just scratch away – ugly, wild scratches.

The only one I show Mum's card to is Janet. She happens to see the black scratches, but she doesn't say anything.

When Dad comes for supper, he says: 'Shall I tell you something beautiful?'

He hears some nice things every day. I wish I had a telephone.

'This afternoon, Aunt Laura, Uncle Alex and Aunt Phyllis were walking in the forest. It was completely white: each twig and each pine-cone was covered with frost. There was no one else, they were enjoying the silence. All of a sudden they saw two peacocks right in front of them, two *white* peacocks, and one of them had its fan wide open!'

'Are there really white peacocks?'

'Yes, this was real. They live on a farm near Aunt Laura but she had never seen them before.'

'Have you got another story?' (This one was so short.)

'Well,' Dad says, 'I've had a shower.'

'All by yourself?'

'Yes. It's a special bathroom, with a chair and all kinds of bars to hold on to.'

He is proud and glad. Does this mean we are going home soon?

Phoebe knows that Mum isn't at home. But our rabbits are!

'I want to eat,' she says all day. 'Give!'

She talks in a funny way, because her brain is still damaged.

'In a minute, Phe.'

'OK.'

One minute later: 'May I eat?'

'In a moment, Phe.'

'All right.'

A moment later: 'I feel like thirsty.'

'In a minute, Phe.'

'All right.'

And so on. According to the doctor it will improve. She can climb into bed. Can she go home now?

Dad says we will have a home help. So all sorts of things are being arranged. So long as I can go with them. Imagine if I had to stay here on my own… Actually, will it really be 'home'?

'How many nights?' Phoebe asks.

'Oh,' says Janet, 'At least another week.'

'How many nights is a week?'

'Seven.'

'Oh, then we're not going home for seven nights. Shame.'

What a shame – she says that a hundred times. And I'm going wild again.

Bill has just arrived. Suddenly I shout to Dad: 'Why did you look back then?'

I'm frightened myself and Dad looks even more shocked, as if he's been hit.

'Do you mean about the accident?'

'Yes!'

For a moment he says nothing. He looks old and tired – serves him right, although it's sad.

'Did I look over my shoulder?' he asks.

'Yes!'

'I don't remember a thing. But when you are driving, you do that often enough, for all sorts of reasons.'

I look at Bill. He nods and says: 'You don't even think about it.'

'But not when there's a *bend*!' I shout.

'No,' says Dad. 'I saw that bend too late.'

'So it's your fault!'

'It was very stupid of me. Sometimes you can't help it. I didn't do it on purpose. It *happened*. Perhaps you or Phoebe asked me something... or perhaps you were larking about...'

'Or you were making jokes...'

'Yes, it can happen in every car, also in the dark and even before a bend. Still, there aren't many accidents. You may think it's horribly stupid, but it's nobody's fault.'

He looks at me so deeply that tears are coming to my

eyes. And to his.

Bill is silent. Phoebe is just playing again.

'OK?' Dad asks.

He doesn't remember about the jokes. Because he was unconscious? I can't remember very well myself.

I suck my thumb. He gets up and leans on my bed, trying to comfort me. At least I've said it, if by accident.

By accident.

That's what he means! Now I understand. You do something but it happens to you.

'Have some sleep now,' Dad says.

'No, because Bill has come to rub our feet and read to us.'

'Oh, wonderful. Goodnight for later then.'

'G'night.'

He goes and hugs Phoebe but she doesn't seem to know what hugs are.

Near the door he waves. 'Sleep tight.'

And I call: 'Shall I wish Mum goodnight too?'

'Of course,' he says. 'Please do.'

'Will you?'

'Yes, inside.'

'Are we going to meet each other then?'

'Yes, that would be great, wouldn't it?'

'Me too,' Phe mumbles.

Thursday, December 31st
and Friday, January 1st

In THE MIDDLE OF THE NIGHT the bandage of the traction is cut open a little – I couldn't stand it anymore. The traction won't be taken off till Monday.

Phoebe is given a little table and chair of her own to do her drawings and puzzles – all day long.

She's talking more and more. When she begins about Mum, she says: 'I must tell you something very sorry.'

Dad has rolled his own wheelchair and he has crutches in his lap. The chair is parked in the corridor and he comes walking into our room.

'Six more nights,' Phoebe says.

Dad hesitates and she nods. 'The nurse said so.'

Phoebe and Dad can walk to the windows together. They say it is beautiful outside. As if I don't know. All my friends are skating. This is the best weather for skating there is. Fathers and mothers go and watch or skate themselves. Or they pull the sledge. They always bring sweets or sandwiches, and gloves and handkerchiefs. When you fall, they can comfort you, and when you *almost* fall, they can see how tough you are.

Aunt Phyllis is reading to us this afternoon and Phoebe says: 'That's what Mum always does. Not any more. She's dead now. Shame, isn't it? Dad says she wanted to die but I didn't.'

'Nor did I,' says Aunt Phyllis. 'But sometimes things happen their own way.'

Miss May has brought lardy cakes. It's a real New Year's Eve.

Phoebe is sitting in Miss May's lap and together we sing all the songs from school. Miss May put them on a tape for us.

So I'm just too busy for sadness and when she is gone, I keep ringing the nurses. It comes back when I'm alone again, when Phe is asleep, and then I don't *want* it to be New Year. What use is all the fussing in this hospital... I like the presents and things, but I'd like to show them to Mum.

'Are we going to watch the fireworks tonight?' I ask Dad.

'Well, only if you get some sleep first.'

'You won't forget to wake us up? Promise!'

'OK, I promise.'

Trudy is with us.

Out of the blue, Phoebe says: 'The rabbits must go inside. Or else they die of the fireworks.'

How clever of her to remember that. Gran's cat is always terrified by the bangs.

Trudy will ring and ask a neighbour to put the rabbits in the shed.

I do feel like sleeping and it's hard for Dad to wake me up.

'Almost midnight,' he whispers in my ear.

With Phoebe it takes even longer.

He hates to wake her, but a promise is a promise.

In the corridor it is dark. I'm yawning and shivering. How weird – New Year's Eve in hospital.

Gran and Grandad have come too. Last year they were at home with us. We saw the best fireworks from my room – the six of us. Just as if it was last week.

'All the children are asleep,' Gran says. 'In fact, no visitors are allowed so late.'

'Only for us?'

'Yes, because you have been here for so long.'

And because Mum is dead, I think.

But now I don't want to think of Mum any more. When will the fireworks start?

'Are the rabbits in the shed?' Phoebe asks.

'Yes. The hutches are on top of each other, because there was no room.'

I feel like going home so much that I even long for the shed, with our bikes, the skippy-balls, rollerskates and all that nice lumber. I can *smell* the straw for the rabbits. Mum has bought this huge bale.

(Thought of Mum after all.)

Midnight!

'Happy New Year,' we all say.

'Is that all right, without Mum?'

'We really must be happy,' Dad says. 'Mum is counting on that. What good is it to her if we stay sad? That would make her miserable.'

We go to the playroom, to see the fireworks better. Nurse Erwin steers my bed, Grandad pushes Dad and Phoebe is on his lap: riding along the corridors like ghost trains.

It's getting terribly foggy, but we are on the sixth floor, and we can see far enough.

Phoebe says: 'This is the prettiest thing I've ever seen.'

There are little red lights that shoot up high and come down slowly.

'Aaahh,' we all say together.

And again Phoebe says: 'This is the prettiest thing I've ever seen.'

Then we get shivery with sleep and the cold. Dad is yawning away.

Back in our room we have a fizzy drink, then I really feel like 'going to bed'.

Gran and Grandad have to drive home now, in the fog and darkness, past the spot of our accident.

The next morning a nurse says: 'You could hardly drive, you couldn't see anything! Sometimes we had to stop and get out.'

All the nurses and patients of 6 East have breakfast

together because it's New Year's Day. Extra snug, with all the stories about the fog. How was it for Gran and Grandad, though?

New Year's Day is a celebration and I *won't* think of Mum. But once in a while I get this feeling that Mum is thinking of me.

Phoebe doesn't dare to say she has a headache. She is afraid they will call a doctor. But she *eats*. When I've had enough, she finishes my bread too. She's had six slices!

She is dressed and wandering about in her little slippers. She hears and sees everything, and gets pretty mad when I ask her to bring me something a dozen times.

So just like in the old days, we are quarrelling again. I wonder if Mum is pleased with that.

Saturday, January 2nd
and Sunday, January 3rd

P HOEBE STILL SAYS, 'I'm hungry' – all day long. It's driving us crazy, because if she eats too much, it will be dangerous. She was on this tube only last week!

Please don't let her be sent home before me. Along with Dad, for example. They *are* talking about it!

On Monday I'll be out of traction.

My hair is driving me crazy too. It's in such a tangle that nobody can deal with it. The nurses call it a bird's nest.

'Comes with rolling around,' they say.

And if they do try to comb it, I scream until they give up. I'm getting on their nerves. I just can't stand it any longer. What if my arm is still wrong?

'Perhaps you should see the hospital hairdresser,' Dad says. 'What about a nice short cut?'

I say 'Yes.' But Mum did such lovely things with my hair. I still feel her soft fingers. I'd never get cross or yell 'ouch' again, if... Too late. I'll never feel her fingers again.

'No,' I say quickly. 'I don't want to go to the hairdresser.'

Janet brings a toasted ham and cheese sandwich, because these are such boring days.

The nurses join in playing games (it's the weekend) and Phoebe is good at *Four in a Row*.

Tomorrow I'll be out of traction.

Monday, January 4th
and Tuesday, January 5th

THE HOLIDAYS ARE OVER; our friends and teachers are back at school – like normal. Mothers take their children. And some fathers.

Uncles, aunts and friends of Mum and Dad are off to work or busy at home. We get fewer visitors but Dad comes and stays longer.

Three weeks ago, Jack came and read to me, when Mum was still in hospital too.

Are we really going on with all the normal, boring things?

I can't believe this is *real*. But now and then Phoebe says: 'I feel like crying' or: 'I think I'm going to cry,' and I know why.

Sometimes she looks quietly at Mum's photos. Sometimes she says: 'I'm thinking of Pete.' (Her rabbit.) And now she's lost Annicka's present: a little box with six tiny puppets from Nicaragua.

I can't help Phoebe right now, they are going to take me out of traction.

The doctor says I mustn't get out of bed yet. He wants to check the x-ray first – like last time…

The nurses let me sit up a little, though. My arm looks ugly. I don't feel like eating and I don't feel like playing.

They bring a doll's house for Phoebe and she'd almost

fit in it herself. Luckily there are lots of toys here.

'In a few nights we're going home,' says Phoebe.

But what if the x-ray is bad again?

I'm not telling anyone that my arm hurts. I'm not saying anything.

Phoebe goes to the bathroom on her own and finishes her vegetables by herself. She could easily go home. Except, she forgets everything. She says 'this woman' instead of Annicka. 'Yesterday' may be five minutes ago or last year. And 'Brother' can mean friend or cousin.

The sun has gone behind a thick cloud, but the edge of that cloud is sparkling, as if Mum is having a peep.

'Mum wanted to see our children,' I tell the nurses. 'And she was going to take us out for late night shopping.'

Sometimes, Mum would take us to a restaurant called *The Pickwick*, where she had coffee and cake, and where children get a surprise. Or we grabble in the lucky bag. Last time I won a ruler.

'I can take you,' Dad says.

But I'm so afraid he will die too.

During the night I'm sick. I keep ringing, because I'm all jittery before the x-ray.

Again we're going to the x-ray department. Then waiting and waiting for the results.

Dad is afraid too, especially when the surgeon comes in. How serious he looks! Or is he gloomy?

My heart is pounding and my throat is aching.

He walks slowly past Phoebe and begins: 'There's a little spot. But that will heal...'

It's OK! I'm cured, I can walk, go home!

'When?'

'Tomorrow or the day after.'

Dad wavers. Tomorrow?

'I think,' says the doctor, 'that Rosemyn could do with an extra day of rehabilitation.'

Dad nods hard.

So the day after tomorrow.

Phoebe is disappointed that her nights won't add up, but 'the day after tomorrow' sounds soon enough.

I have a bath, my hair is washed with a special shampoo for the tangles, and the bird's nest is combed out. I keep quiet and get a nice brooch. We are all proud and relieved.

Phoebe's doctor says he needs to do another EEG of her brain. We don't know why, but when Phe is sick tonight, I understand: she is scared of everything unfamiliar. Last time she was still unconscious.

Once more I tell Dad: 'Don't talk about Mum.'

And Phoebe says again: 'I think I need to cry.'

'Because Mum is dead?' Dad asks.

'No. About something else... I'm afraid of something… It's happening soon. To me. The man said so, who comes here.'

'Oh, you mean the EEG. That's a kind of x-ray, a special photo of your head. Just like Rose had, remember? That's not frightening. Shall I come with you?'

'Yes.'

Bill has come for the last time.

When he's about to leave, he helps me to lie straight again, holding me by the arms.

'Ouch! My arm!'

We are both shocked and Bill fetches Mary Ann.

He says: 'I held her awkwardly, under the armpits… She looks so normal, without the traction. I feel so bad about it.'

'Does it hurt?' Mary Ann asks.

'Nah.'

It does hurt, but that's rotten for Bill. And the bone is healed, isn't it? I'll just sleep.

Wednesday, January 6th
and Thursday, January 7th

THE PAIN IN MY ARM is almost gone. I have a nice bath, with Phoebe, and walk where I want all day. There's not much left to be done, only pack our things.

It's tough on Phe, though, this EEG. She's peed in bed.

Dad has come extra early.

The nurse has a book of pictures, to explain about the EEG, but Dad doesn't want Phoebe to see them. He lets *me* look at them. Some are pretty frightening.

Phoebe is taken away, bed and all, and Dad follows quickly in his wheelchair.

They come back worn out.

'Was it nasty?'

Phoebe shakes her head but I'm not sure.

'The nurses were really proud of her,' Dad says. 'She was great.'

Phoebe nods.

The frost is over. Annicka has come cycling in the rain, with the boys. They bring a homemade Twelfth-night-cake with three peas hidden in it and the person who gets a pea in their slice may choose a prize.

We're all together in the playroom and Annicka cuts about twenty thick slices. We can eat as many as we want. But I don't get a pea.

Then we have to pack our things. There are so many that we don't know how to begin – it's like moving house.

The boys take all the postcards and drawings off the walls, go and ask for plastic bags, put the things together, go and fetch a trolley from 5 West (which is actually for medicines), Annicka is sorting through our clothes, Phe and I say which presents are hers or mine and Dad is in the middle of the room, arranging and gathering.

Dad keeps saying: 'Careful,' or: 'Watch out for your arm.' But we're cured!

He asks: 'What are you wearing tomorrow?'

'I don't know. What happened to our other clothes? The ones we were wearing then?'

Dad hesitates. 'They had to cut them up.'

'Cut them up? Why! Our most beautiful clothes!'

'They couldn't take your coat or blouse off with your broken arm, could they? That had to be done as fast as possible, because they didn't know how bad the injuries were. I couldn't even breathe…'

I know. That's not the point! Mum and I had chosen those clothes together. We were going to a party! I remember exactly what Mum was wearing. What happened to her skirt and cardigan?

It's just as if they have cut into us.

After supper Phe and I are fooling about, the two of us. We build a sort of slide on my bed and we are whizzing down like mad, screaming, falling over and doubling up with the giggles.

When Dad arrives, he is scared stiff.

We don't calm down until we talk about home.

Phoebe asks: 'What kind of Mum do we get now?'

'A home help. She's very kind.'

'What's her name?'

'I don't know yet.'

'Karen and Rianne,' Phe says.

Jack arrives and Phoebe says: 'What have you come for? Ah, I know: to read to us.'

'No,' he says, 'to bring your shoes, for tomorrow.'

'Oh, my prettiest!'

She strokes the fur edges and puts them neatly under her bed.

Jack takes a lot of our things with him now, so there won't be too much tomorrow.

'Who is taking us home?' I ask Dad.

'Well, who shall we ask?'

'Aunt Laura.'

'OK. I hope she's at home. Do you know that Ann and Trish have cleaned our whole house? It's all ready, waiting for us.'

'And Pete,' says Phe. 'I'm going to hug him all day.'

What will I do first? There is so much. At times I'm afraid to think of it. Dad is still a cripple.

Trudy has come for our last 'bedtime' in hospital – what a funny feeling.

I thought I wouldn't be able to sleep, but before I know it, I wake up at the normal hour.

It's terribly busy: breakfast, a bath, a hairwash, packing the last things and we are weighed. Then Dad, Aunt Laura and Elise arrive.

Dad is dressed normally. But I haven't got time to look at him and there is no time to say goodbye to everybody – we're going home!

The wheelchair is full of bags and we also need another trolley from 5 West.

All the nurses are waving in the corridor. How much I've been through with them. As if Mum died *here*. And probably I'll never see them again.

We wave back. Then out of the corridor, into the lift, along another corridor, through big revolving doors. Outside!

It's raining a bit. Dad is glad the frost is over. Aunt Laura fetches the car.

Dad sits down like an old man, with his crutches and everything.

We are going round the back of the house. Our house.

I want to be everywhere at the same time: in the shed (no cycling allowed yet), in the garden (where did Mum plant those bulbs again?), with the rabbits and in the house, downstairs and upstairs.

In the living room there are all kinds of flowers, postcards and drawings – a huge one from Muriel and Donovan: WELCOME. In the kitchen the coffee is ready, with two cakes.

I run around the house again, lie down on my bed, rummage in the cupboards and my desk…

Not in Mum's room.

Phoebe tries to take her rabbit on her lap, but he's forgotten her and he's grown too big for her. He struggles, she can't hold him… Now she's got a scratch on her hand.

Elise gives us *Four in a Row* and we start playing it right away.

Aunt Laura gives us yellow roses, which brings a lot of tears to Dad's eyes.

All day people come with flowers and presents. They also buy food for us and help with tea, the dishes and taking us to bed.

Dad comes in to say goodnight and goes to bed himself.

Although I miss Mum in a way I can't say, it's been a happy day. I think Mum is pleased.

Can I still talk to her now?

It's such a shame about your goodnight songs. Nobody knows those long and beautiful ones, and so many… Keeping my eyes closed, I can hear you sing.

You've got these songbooks, haven't you? I know where they are. I'll show them to Dad. So he can learn them; after all he can play the piano too. Or perhaps not. They really go with you.

It's nice to be back in my own bed. Do you know what I wanted to ask? Don't you miss your bed? So silly.

Remember what Dad always says? Goodnight, sleep tight, sweet dreams, say hello for me to the angels, see you tomorrow, now hush.

I wish I knew a lot more of those words.

I repeat them all and then he always says: Now *really* hush.